CRITICAL THINKING

Merrill
Physics
*Principles
and Problems*

CONTENT CONSULTANT

Frank Kokai
Physics Teacher
Upper Arlington High School
Upper Arlington, Ohio

GLENCOE
Macmillan/McGraw-Hill

New York, New York   Columbus, Ohio   Mission Hills, California   Peoria, Illinois

A Glencoe/McGraw-Hill Program

Merrill Physics: Principles & Problems

Student Edition

Teacher Wraparound Edition

Problems and Solutions Manual

Teacher Resource Package

Transparency Package

Laboratory Manual:
 Student and Teacher Editions

Study Guide, Student Edition

Lesson Plan Booklet

English/Spanish Glossary

Computer Test Bank

These masters offer an opportunity to apply critical thinking process skills to extend content knowledge and skill development beyond the scope of the text. Some of the masters involve hands-on activities. These masters are identified in the Table of Contents. Most of the materials used are commonly available and are listed on the individual masters.

ISBN 0-02-826737-0

Copyright 1995, 1992, 1990 by the Glencoe Division of Macmillan/McGraw-Hill Publishing Company.

Send all inquiries to: **GLENCOE DIVISION, Macmillan/McGraw-Hill**
936 Eastwind Drive
Westerville, Ohio 43081

Printed in the United States of America

1 2 3 4 5 6 7 8 9 MAL 99 98 97 96 95 94

Contents

*These masters involve hands-on activities. Materials required are listed on each master.

CHAPTER 1 : Critical Thinking

SUPERCONDUCTIVITY

Superconductors are materials that have no resistance to conducting an electrical current. Many materials become superconductors at very low temperatures. The temperature at which a material becomes a superconductor is called the *transition temperature*. The scale below shows the transition temperature for several substances.

1. What range of temperatures is shown on the scale?

2. What is the value of absolute zero on the scale?

3. Estimate the transition temperature (to the nearest degree Celsius) of niobium nitride.

4. At what temperature does lead become a superconductor?

5. Which substance becomes a superconductor at a higher temperature, tin or niobium-tin?

6. Rank the following substances in order of decreasing transition temperature: vanadium, aluminum, technetium, and thallium.

7. Which substance needs to be cooled the most to become a superconductor? What is its transition temperature?

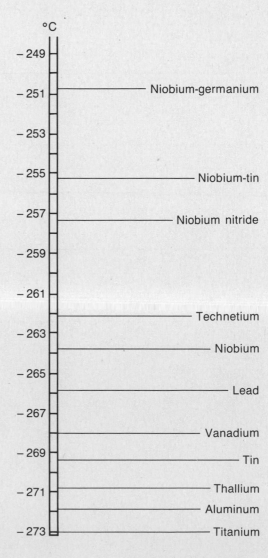

CHAPTER 2 : Critical Thinking

DIRECT AND INDIRECT MEASUREMENTS

Materials

100-mL graduated cylinder   vernier caliper or metric ruler
dried beans

Procedure

Use a vernier caliper or metric ruler to measure the thickness of three different beans. Record your data in Table 1 and find the average thickness. Use a graduated cylinder to measure the volume of some beans. Then spread the beans in a single layer on a tabletop, and arrange the beans so that they form the smallest possible circle. You have formed a cylinder with a height equal to the thickness of one bean. Measure the diameter of this cylinder. Repeat this procedure twice, using different numbers of beans each time. Record your data in Table 2. The equation for the volume of a cylinder is $V = \pi r^2 h$. Solve the equation for h, and find the average value.

Results

Table 1

Sample data are given.

Bean	h (cm)
1	
2	
3	
Average	

Table 2

Trial	Volume (cm³)	Diameter (cm)	Radius (cm)	h (cm)
1				
2				
3				
Average				

1. Which measurement is a direct measurement?

2. Which measurement is an indirect measurement?

3. Which method gives the more accurate measurement of the thickness of a bean?

4. What are some sources of error in making the indirect measurement? How might these sources of error be reduced?

5. When might indirect measurements be useful? Give an example.

CHAPTER
3 Critical Thinking

POSITIONS ALONG A ROLLER COASTER

You have seen position-time graphs that illustrate movement in one direction. But how would you diagram movement in more than one direction, as in a roller coaster? The position-time information shown is for a trip on a very small roller coaster. The position information describes horizontal movement along the ground and vertical movement up in the air.

Time (s)	Horizontal Position (m)	Vertical Position (m)
1	0	11
2	1	11
3	2	11
4	4	8
5	7	5
6	11	1
7	17	0
8	21	2
9	22	5
10	21	8
11	17	10
12	13	8
13	12	5
14	13	2
15	17	0
16	21	0
17	24	0
18	27	3
19	29	5
20	31	7
21	33	7
22	35	5
23	38	2
24	40	0

1. Using graph paper, plot a position-time graph for the movement along the ground. Describe the curve.

2. Is the velocity constant?

3. Describe the velocity at 9 seconds and at 13 seconds.

4. What would you see if you were in a balloon above the roller coaster and could not see any vertical movement, only movement along the ground?

5. Using another sheet of graph paper, plot a position-time graph for the vertical movement. Describe the curve.

6. Is this velocity constant?

7. How would you describe this motion?

8. If you were standing at the very end of the roller coaster, watching as the car came straight toward you, what kind of movement would you see?

9. Using a third sheet of graph paper, plot the position along the ground against the position above the ground. Use the same scale on each axis, and plot the distance along the ground as the x-axis. This graph will represent the position of the car at each point in time. After you have plotted the points, connect them in the correct time sequence. What does the shape of the graph represent?

10. Describe the shape of the roller coaster.

11. Now that you know the shape of the roller coaster, what was happening between 7 and 15 seconds? Between 17 and 24 seconds?

CHAPTER 4 : Critical Thinking

ACCELERATION AND ESCAPE VELOCITY

During the twenty-first century, journeys may be made to and from Mars. In the years that follow, other objects in the solar system may become the targets for round-trip explorations by spacecraft. Many obstacles will have to be overcome to achieve successful round trips. One of the most formidable of these will be to accelerate the spacecraft to the velocity required for them to escape the gravitational attraction of the object on which they have landed. This value, called *escape velocity*, must be reached in a reasonable amount of time. For the purposes of this activity, assume that the required time is 1000 seconds.

Based on the above criterion and the data in the table below, answer the questions that follow.

1. Assuming that the masses of all spacecraft are equal, predict from which object escape would be most difficult. From which object would escape be least difficult?

Table 1

Object	Velocity (km/s)	Acceleration required (km/s^2)
Mercury	4.2	
Venus	10.0	
Mars	5.0	
Earth	11.3	
Moon	2.4	
Jupiter	59.7	
Saturn	35.4	
Uranus	24.1	
Neptune	24.1	

2. If the rockets used to boost the spacecraft from each of these objects produced constant acceleration, what would be the shape of the curve on a velocity-time graph in each case?

3. Which curve would have the greatest slope?

4. Calculate the constant acceleration required to reach each escape velocity in 1000.0 s. Show your calculations.

5. Is your prediction in Question 1 supported? Explain your answer.

6. Based on your observations from films or videos of space flights, how do you think achievement of escape velocity in such flights differs from that assumed in Question 2?

CHAPTER
5
Critical Thinking

FORCES AND FLIGHT

The four forces that act on an airplane in flight are thrust, drag, lift, and weight. When the propellers of the airplane turn, they exert a force that pushes air backward. The air exerts an equal force on the propellers, forcing them, and the airplane, forward. This forward force is thrust. Drag is caused by the air. As the airplane moves forward, this force acts in a backward direction. Lift is an upward force caused by the movement of air over the wings of the airplane. The amount of lift is related to the shape of the wing and the forward velocity of the airplane. The faster the airplane moves, the greater the lift force. Weight is a downward force caused by gravity. The greater the mass of the airplane and its contents, the greater the downward force.

1. Which of the forces described form a pair of action-reaction forces? Which of Newton's laws describes such a pair of forces?

2. Which two forces must be balanced if the airplane is to fly at a constant forward velocity? Which of Newtons's laws describes such balanced forces?

3. Which two forces must be balanced if the airplane is to fly at a constant altitude?

4. To take off, an airplane must accelerate until its forward velocity gives it enough lift to get off the ground. What are two ways in which the mass of the airplane affects takeoff?

5. Flaps on the airplane wings can be moved to change the shape of the wings. During landing, the flaps decrease lift and increase drag. How do these changes help the airplane to land?

6. As the airplane moves through the air, two factors cause drag. What are they? Why do they cause drag to be greater at lower altitudes?

Critical Thinking

MEASURING HEIGHT INDIRECTLY

Materials

string
protractor
meter stick
tape
metric tape measure
large-diameter drinking straw
washer or other weight

Procedure

Work with a partner. Hold a meter stick on end so that it is perpendicular to the floor. You may wish to tape or clamp the meter stick to an upright support. Hold one end of a piece of string on the top of the meter stick, and have your partner extend the string to the floor in front of the meter stick. The string should be held as taut as possible. Your partner will measure the angle between the floor and the string, the distance along the floor from the meter stick to the point where the string touches the floor, and the length of the string. Record these measurements in Table 1. Use your data to calculate the height of the meter stick. There are three different methods to use. Compare your calculations with the known height of the meter stick.

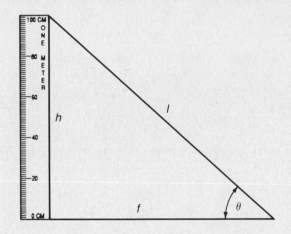

Make a clinometer like the one shown in the drawing. Tape a protractor to a drinking straw so that the straw is at a right angle to the base of the protractor. Tape a weighted string to the protractor. Be sure that the string can swing freely. When you look through the straw at an object, the position of the string against the protractor will show the angle between your line of sight and the horizontal. CAUTION: *Never look at the sun or any other bright object through the clinometer.*

Using your clinometer and a tape measure, you can indirectly measure the height of objects such as buildings or trees. Devise a procedure to make indirect measurements. Test your procedure by calculating the height of a structure of known height, such as the school building or a flagpole.

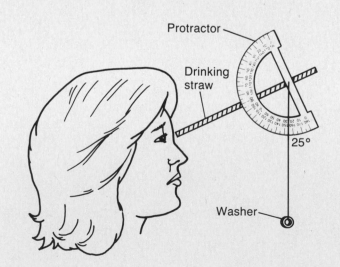

Critical Thinking

NAME _____

Results
Table 1

Length of string (m)	
Distance along floor (m)	
Angle	
Height (use angle and length of string)	
Height (use angle and distance along floor) (m)	
Height (use Pythagorean theorem) (m)	
Height (known value) (m)	

1. List the steps of your method for using a clinometer.

2. Why is this method more practical than the string method?

3. Notice that Table 2 includes a column headed "Corrected height." What measurement must be added to the calculated height? How could you avoid having to make this correction?

Table 2

Object	Distance (m)	Angle	Height (m)	Corrected height (m)

CHAPTER 7 : Critical Thinking

MECHANICAL RESONANCE

Materials

two vertical lab supports or ring stands
string
two weights

Procedure

If you suspend a weight from a string and push on the weight, it will swing back and forth in simple harmonic motion. If you want to increase the amplitude of the swing, you can do so by pushing on the swinging weight at a specific time in its swing. This effect is known as mechanical resonance. To investigate this effect, tie a string between two vertical supports, and then use a second piece of string and a weight to form a pendulum that hangs from the string. Set the pendulum in motion and observe its behavior. Try to increase the amplitude of the pendulum by applying a small force at regular intervals of time.

Use another piece of string and a second weight to suspend another pendulum from the horizontal string. The two pendulums should be the same length. Start only one pendulum moving and note what happens. Try this again, but vary the length of one of the pendulums.

Results

1. When you had only one pendulum set up, what was the best time in its motion to add the extra force?

2. Describe what happened when you had two pendulums of identical length, and started one moving.

3. What caused the resonance effect you saw?

4. Could you get the same effect when the pendulums were of different lengths? Explain your answer.

5. In all cases, the pendulums eventually stop moving. Why?

CHAPTER

8 : Critical Thinking

ACCELERATION DUE TO GRAVITY

Isaac Newton made a number of contributions to our knowledge of gravitation and the variables that account for its effects. Table 1 contains data about the sun and the nine planets of the solar system. Analyze the data carefully. To help you do this, complete Table 2. Then answer the questions that follow.

Table 1

Object	Mass (kg)	Acceleration due to gravity (m/s^2)
Sun	1.991×10^{30}	293.0
Mercury	3.2×10^{23}	3.72
Venus	4.88×10^{24}	8.82
Earth	5.979×10^{21}	9.80
Mars	6.42×10^{23}	3.72
Jupiter	1.901×10^{27}	24.8
Saturn	5.68×10^{26}	10.5
Uranus	8.68×10^{25}	9.01
Neptune	1.03×10^{26}	11.7
Pluto	1.15×10^{22}	0.49

Table 2

Object (in order of decreasing mass)	Object (in order of decreasing acceleration due to gravity)

1. Based on the data, what generalization seems most appropriate?

2. Are there exceptions to the generalization?

3. If there are exceptions in Question 2, how might you account for these?

4. In what way would your weight vary, if at all, if you were to find yourself on each of the objects represented in the table? Explain your answer.

5. From which object would the least energy be required to launch a projectile into space? Explain your answer.

CHAPTER 9 : Critical Thinking

HIGHWAY BARRIERS

Anyone who has driven down a major highway on a long journey has encountered places where relatively sudden forks in the highway demand quick decisions. Highway safety experts know that drivers approaching such a fork at high speed have become confused, lost control of their vehicle, and plowed into the apex of the concrete divider which separates the diverging roads. The result has often been a serious or deadly accident.

Since the advent of freeways, superhighways, and other high-speed roads, safety engineers have tried to improve the safety of road travel by doing such things as improving lighting and road signs. Nevertheless, drivers still got confused and found themselves hurtling toward a virtually immovable concrete barrier and certain injury or death. Another solution had to be invented—and it was. The invention, a series of cans filled with sand and placed in front of the concrete barrier, was the idea of a former race car driver named John Fitch. Appropriately, the arrays of such cans are called "Fitch Inertial Barriers." In this exercise, you will explore practical applications of Fitch's invention. Assume that the only variable in the construction of the automobiles in the table is mass and that the occupants of the cars are of equal mass.

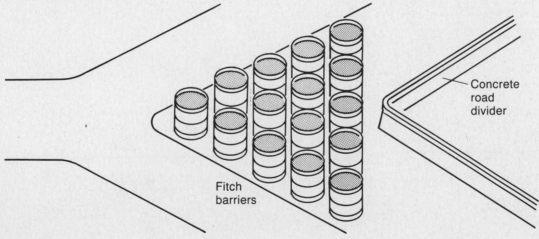

Table 1

Automobile	Mass (kg)	Velocity (km/h)
1	910	82
2	1675	29
3	1200	50
4	1350	63
5	1500	40

1. What general principle accounts for the safety features of the Fitch barriers?

2. Which automobile will penetrate most deeply into the array of Fitch barriers? Explain your answers.

3. Which automobile will penetrate least deeply into the array of Fitch barriers? Explain your answer.

4. Considering only automobiles 3 and 5, the occupants of which of these cars are least likely to sustain serious injuries? Explain your answers.

5. If the Fitch barriers were absent, the occupants of which car would be most likely to sustain serious injuries? Assume the concrete divider is an immovable object. Explain your answer.

6. If the Fitch barriers were absent, the occupants of which automobile would be least likely to sustain serious injuries? Explain your answer.

CHAPTER 10 : Critical Thinking

BICYCLE GEARS

Materials

ten-speed bicycle

Procedure

On a ten-speed bicycle, there are two gears at the pedals and five at the rear wheel, producing ten different combinations, or gear ratios. To see how the gears work, turn the bicycle upside down. Turn the pedal and count the number of times the rear wheel turns for each turn of the pedal. Try this in first, fifth, and tenth gears, and note which combination of front and rear gears is in use.

Count the teeth on each of the front gears and record these data in Table 1. Count the teeth on each of the rear gears and record these data. Calculate the ratio of the number of teeth on the front gear to the number of teeth on the rear gear.

Results
Table 1

Gear	Front Large	Small	Rear A (largest)	B	C	D	E (smallest)
Number of teeth							
Ratio with large gear							
Ratio with small gear							

1. How does the force on the pedal vary in first, fifth, and tenth gears?

2. How many revolutions of the rear wheel were there for one revolution of the pedals in first, fifth, and tenth gears? How does the ratio of revolutions compare to the gear ratios?

3. What gear combination would you use to climb hills? Explain your answer.

4. What gear combination would you use to maintain a high speed on a flat, level road? Explain your answer.

5. A machine can multiply force or speed, but not both. Explain how the bicycle demonstrates this statement.

CHAPTER 11 : Critical Thinking

ENDLESS ENERGY?

You know that energy is conserved. You have seen examples of energy changing from one form to another in a seemingly endless chain. If that is true, can someone make a machine that could go on forever? Throughout history, people have dreamed of a machine like this. Once you put energy in, the machine would run itself. It would be like getting something for nothing!

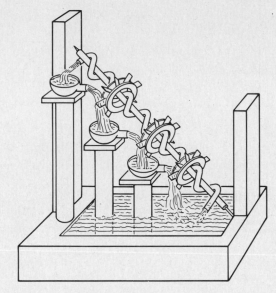

The diagram shows a sixteenth-century design for a "perpetual motion" water pump. The diagonal part is based on an ancient device that actually did work. It had a spiral channel that filled with water when the screw was turned. The perpetual motion version of the pump was supposed to eliminate the work of turning the screw. The sixteenth-century inventor added a series of tiny paddles. When water falling from the top of the screw hit the paddles, it would power the pump. Look closely at the diagram, and think about it in terms of energy.

1. What form of energy has the water gained on reaching the top of the spiral?

2. What kind of energy would the water have when it falls onto the paddles? What does this energy do next?

3. What could cause this device to run out of energy? Where does the energy go?

4. Dream up a perpetual motion machine that you yourself could use. First, decide what you want the machine to do. Make a simple diagram of your idea.

CHAPTER 12 : Critical Thinking

COMPARING HEAT ENGINES

In your text you have seen a diagram of an automobile's gasoline engine. This engine is called a four-stroke engine because there are four strokes, or movements, of the piston in each fuel-burning cycle. The diesel engine, shown in the diagram on this page, is another kind of four-stroke engine. The greatest difference between the diesel engine and the gasoline engine is that the diesel engine does not use a spark plug to ignite the fuel. The air in the cylinder is compressed so much that when the fuel enters the cylinder, the high temperature of the air causes the fuel to ignite spontaneously. The diesel engine does not burn gasoline. Instead it burns diesel fuel, which is a less refined hydrocarbon.

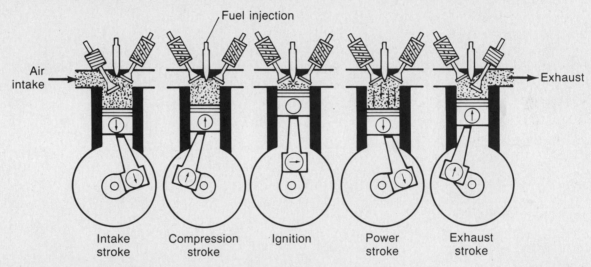

1. In the first stroke of a gasoline engine, a mixture of gasoline and air enters the cylinder. This mixture is controlled by a device called a carburetor. How is the first stroke in a diesel engine different?

2. Does a diesel engine need a carburetor? Explain your answer.

3. In the second stroke of each engine, the contents of the cylinder are compressed. What else happens during the compression stroke in the diesel engine?

4. What energy change takes place during the third stroke in each engine?

5. What happens during the fourth stroke in the diesel engine? How does this compare with the fourth stroke in the gasoline engine?

6. Why would a diesel engine be less expensive to run than a gasoline engine?

7. A diesel engine is heavier than a gasoline engine of comparable size. Explain why.

8. Although diesel engines are heavier than gasoline engines, they are more efficient. This trade-off makes them a good choice for trucks and locomotives. Explain why.

9. Sometimes the cylinders of a gasoline engine fire just after the ignition is turned off. This post-ignition spark is sometimes referred to as "dieseling." Explain why this term is appropriate.

CHAPTER
13 Critical Thinking

THE EFFECT OF THERMAL EXPANSION ON LAKES

Most liquids expand as they are heated and contract as they are cooled. As a result, a liquid is densest just before it freezes. Water is an exception to this rule, reaching a maximum density at 4°C. Because water at its freezing point is less dense than water between 0°C and 4°C, lakes freeze at the top. In most areas with a moderate climate, lakes do not freeze all the way to the bottom, and water at the bottom of the lake is a few degrees warmer than the ice at the top. Because water at each temperature has a different density, the lake develops layers of water.

When spring arrives, the ice melts and the water begins to warm. The water at the top of the lake warms first. When it reaches 4°C, the water falls to the bottom, creating a convection current. The lake is said to "turn over." This spring turnover is important for the organisms living in the lake. As the water moves, nutrients that have settled to the bottom become mixed into the water and become available to the organisms in the water. Also, oxygen from the air enters the surface water and is carried to the bottom of the lake as the lake turns over.

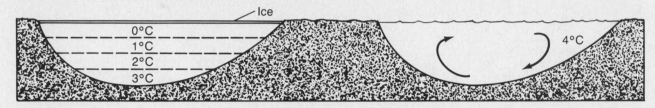

1. The drawing at the left shows the lake in winter. What is the temperature of the water just below the ice? What is the temperature at the bottom?

2. The drawing at the right shows the lake during the spring turnover. Describe the temperature distribution of the lake during the turnover.

3. As summer approaches, the lake again forms a layered pattern of temperature distribution. What are the main sources of heat for the lake? What part of the lake warms first?

4. When the summer layers have formed, water temperatures may range from 12°C to 24°C. Where will the densest water be? Where will the warmest water be? Where will the coolest water be?

5. In the late fall a second turnover takes place. What one condition must exist for the turnover to occur? What causes this condition?

CHAPTER 14 : Critical Thinking

WAVE SUPERPOSITION

The diagram shows two periodic transverse waves traveling along a taut string in the same direction at the same time. According to the principle of superposition, interference between these two waves will produce a resultant wave. Study the diagram and compare the two waves. Look for points where maximum constructive interference would occur. Also look for points where maximum destructive interference would occur.

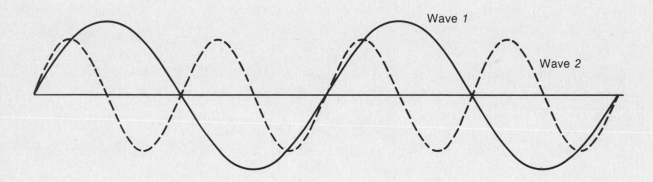

Wave 1

Wave 2

1. Which of the two waves has the greater amplitude?

2. If the frequency of wave **1** is f_1 and the frequency of wave **2** is f_2, state the numerical relationship between the frequencies in the form of an equation.

3. If the wavelength of wave **1** is λ_1 and the wavelength of wave **2** is λ_2, state the numerical relationship between the wavelengths in the form of an equation.

4. State the principle of superposition. On the figure, sketch the resultant wave produced by the superposition of the two waves. Then label with a "C" the parts of the wave produced by constructive interference and with a "D" the parts of the wave produced by destructive interference.

CHAPTER

15

Critical Thinking

TUNING A GUITAR

Materials

guitar

Procedure

When a guitar is tuned, the musician begins with the top string, which is the thickest, and plays the lowest note. By holding the string against one of the small ridges, or frets, on the neck of the guitar, the musician raises the pitch of the sound made by the string. The thickest string is held against the fifth fret, and the next string is tightened or loosened until its pitch matches the thickest string. Each string is tuned in a similar manner, until the last string is in tune.

Beats are variations in amplitude caused by two sounds of close, but not identical, frequency. Listening for beats is a way to tell if two guitar strings are in tune. Start with a properly tuned guitar, and use the first and second strings. Hold the first string against the fifth fret, and then pluck both the first and second strings. They should play the same note. Try this again, and while the strings are vibrating, change the tension of the second string, and listen for beats.

Results

1. Do you hear beats when the two strings are properly in tune? Explain your answer.

2. What happens to the frequency of the beats as you adjust the second string further out of tune?

3. Do the number of beats tell you if the pitch of the second string is higher or lower than the pitch of the first string?

4. Re-tune the guitar, hold the first string against the fifth fret and pluck it. Then quickly stop its vibration. Explain what you hear after the vibration of the first string is stopped.

5. Repeat the procedure in Question 4, but hold the first string at the fourth fret. Do you hear the same effect? Explain your answer.

6. How can beats and resonance be used to find out if a guitar is in tune?

CHAPTER 16 : Critical Thinking

USING LIGHT TO ESTIMATE DISTANCE

Imagine that you have taken a camping trip to the Rocky Mountains with five friends. On a quiet evening when there seems to be nothing exciting to do, you decide to perform a seemingly impossible feat. You announce the following to your friends.

"I will climb that mountain five miles to the north taking with me only a pad of paper, a pencil, and a super-sensitive light meter that measures illuminance. Here are five identical flashlights. Beginning at 11:00 PM you may walk, jog, or run directly toward or away from me for one hour, or you may stay where you are. At midnight, stand still and shine the flashlights at me for a few seconds. Resume walking, jogging, running, or standing still for another hour till 1:00 AM. Flash your lights at me again. Then repeat the whole procedure for one more hour. I only ask that you line up from left to right and keep these relative positions so I can identify you by assigning you code numbers from 1 to 6. I'll come back to camp shortly after 2:00 AM and you can ask me questions about your activities between midnight and 2:00 AM. And I will answer every question correctly."

You head for the mountain, climb to the top, and over the next few hours collect the data shown. What are your answers to your friends' questions? Explain each answer.

1. At midnight, which of us was closest to you?

2. At midnight, which of us was farthest from you?

3. From midnight to 2:00 AM, one of us did not appear to move. Which one?

Table 1

Friend	ILLUMINANCE (lm/m²)		
	Midnight	1:00 AM	2:00 AM
1	16	16	16
2	4	9	16
3	4	9	9
4	1	1	4
5	36	4	9

4. From midnight to 1:00 AM, which of us traveled the greatest distance?

5. Which of us appeared to move continuously between midnight and 2:00 AM?

6. Which of us appeared to be in continuous motion *towards* you?

CHAPTER 17 : Critical Thinking

THE SHAPE OF A DIAMOND

The brilliance of a diamond depends on a number of factors. Among these is the way light is reflected and refracted by the diamond. If light were completely reflected by the surface of a diamond, it would simply act as a mirror and would be of no value as a gem. By the same token if light, once entering a diamond, were to be reflected endlessly within the diamond or escape from its bottom or lower sides, the diamond would also be of little value as a gem. Knowing this, a diamond cutter must produce a stone with 58 facets—or exterior surface planes—that form precise angles with one another. The cutter does this in such a way that the maximum amount of light entering the diamond leaves the facets near the top of the gem.

Based on the fact that the index of refraction of a diamond is 2.42, examine the following three simplified drawings of cut diamonds and answer the questions that follow. The only tool you will need is a protractor.

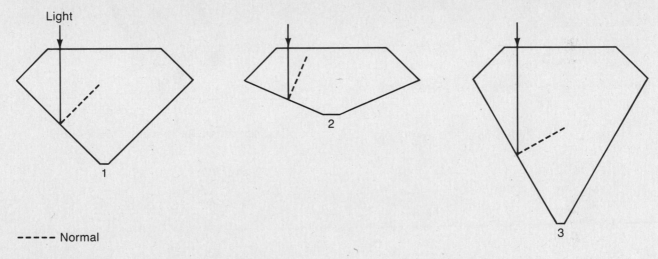

Light

1

2

3

- - - - - Normal

1. What datum must you first calculate?

2. How can you accomplish this calculation?

3. What is the numerical value of this datum?

4. Which of the diamonds is most correctly cut? Explain your answer.

5. To support your answer, complete each illustration by drawing its ray diagram.

CHAPTER
18
**Critical
Thinking**

REFLECTING TELESCOPES

Various optical instruments have been invented to make distant objects appear nearer and larger than they actually are. Among these are a variety of telescopes and binoculars. Some consist solely of lenses while others combine lenses and mirrors. Two different kinds of reflecting telescopes are shown. How do they work? To find the answers, complete each ray diagram. Then answer the questions that follow.

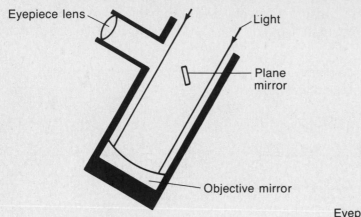

Newtonian Reflecting Telescope   **Cassegrainian Reflecting Telescope**

1. Why would these telescopes be impractical to view objects on Earth?

2. How does the size of the objective mirror affect the performance of these telescopes?

3. What components of the telescope determine the magnification? Explain your answer.

CHAPTER
19 : **Critical Thinking**

DIFFRACTION

Materials

2 single-edged razor blades
straight filament lamp (showcase lamp)
cardboard

tape
thread

colored filters (red, green or blue
cellophane or spotlight gelatin)

Procedure

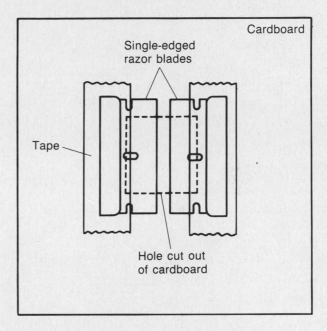

Cut out a 2 cm × 2 cm square hole in a small sheet of cardboard. Tape the razor blades over the hole as shown. CAUTION: *Handle the razor blades with extreme care.* While holding the cardboard so the slit is vertical, stand 1–2 m from the lamp and observe the illuminated lamp through the slit. Repeat the procedure covering the slit in turn with various colored filters.

Next, place a length of thread vertically between the edges of the razor blades and tape the ends of the thread to the cardboard. The space between the razor blades should now be a double slit. Observe the lamp through the double slit. Repeat your observation with various colored filters covering the slit.

Results

1. Describe what you saw when looking at the lamp through a single slit with no colored filters. Describe what you saw when looking at the lamp through a single slit covered with colored filters.

2. Describe what you saw when looking at the lamp through a double slit with no colored filters. Describe what you saw when looking at the lamp through a double slit covered with colored filters.

3. Do your observations support the hypothesis that light possesses the properties of waves? Explain how the evidence you have uncovered supports your answer.

4. How does the color of the filters affect your observations? Explain any variations observed.

CHAPTER 20 : Critical Thinking

LIGHTNING

Using the *Reader's Guide to Periodical Literature* in your school library, find articles dealing with lightning. Read several of them to help you answer the following questions about lightning. List your reference at the end of each answer.

1. What are the chances of survival if you are struck by lightning?

2. How does the number of deaths caused by lightning compare with the number of deaths due to other weather events such as tornadoes and hurricanes?

3. What are some safety rules when dealing with lightning?

4. How does a lightning rod protect a house?

5. Identify each of the following types of lightning.
   a. forked lightning

   b. sheet lightning

   c. heat lightning

   d. bead or chain lightning

CHAPTER 21

Critical Thinking

A JARFUL OF CHANGE

Electric charges can be collected in a jar. The drawing shows a Leyden jar. It is made by covering the inner and outer surfaces of a glass jar with separate pieces of metal foil. A metal rod, with a metal knob at the end, protrudes through the stopper on top of the jar, and a metal chain connected to the rod touches the metal foil inside the jar. If a rubber rod is rubbed with fur and touched to the metal knob on the top of the Leyden jar, a negative charge is transferred to the inside of the jar. A positive charge develops on the outside of the jar.

1. On the drawing provided, show the charge distribution on all metal parts of the Leyden jar.

2. Contrast the way a charge is given to the inside of the jar with the way a charge is given to the outside of the jar.

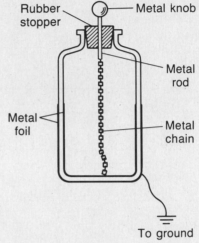

3. Why must separate pieces of metal foil be used to cover the two surfaces of the jar?

4. Why would the jar be unable to hold charges if there were no metal foil on the inside and outside of the jar?

5. What is the purpose of connecting the outside of the jar to the ground?

6. Why would it be dangerous for you to touch the outside of the Leyden jar and the metal knob at the same time?

7. Why are birds and squirrels able to sit on overhead electric wires without being electrocuted?

CHAPTER
22 Critical Thinking

FUTURE ENERGY USES

A highly industrialized society such as that of the United States requires tremendous amounts of energy to provide for the needs of its people. Most of the energy is made available from four sources: oil, coal, natural gas, and electricity. Moreover, the first two sources, oil and coal, are used to produce a large proportion of the electricity consumed in the United States.

Scientists, engineers, and conservationists have made many predictions concerning the future energy needs of the United States and how those energy needs might be satisfied. The table is an adaptation of one such projection. Increases in energy use are projected for the year 2010, taking into account various possible energy policies. "Other uses" include energy that is wasted. Examine the table and then answer the questions that follow.

Table 1

	Projected Energy Use				
Energy conservation policy	Buildings (%)	Industry (%)	Transport (%)	Other uses (%)	Increase from 1975 (%)
1. Make major lifestyle changes.	10.3	44.8	17.2	27.7	81.7
2. Make some lifestyle changes.	13.5	37.8	18.9	29.8	104.2
3. Slowly increase energy-producing efficiency.	13.8	35.1	21.3	29.8	132.4
4. Do not change present policies.	14.7	28.7	19.1	37.5	234.5

1. With regard to energy waste, what two policies produce the same result? What might explain this fact?

2. What factor is projected to increase, regardless of the policy adopted? What reasons might you suggest for this?

3. Give your interpretation of "major lifestyle changes."

4. Give your interpretation of "some lifestyle changes."

5. A very large proportion of the energy produced today to meet the demands listed in the table come from the burning of fossil fuels. Choose one alternate source of energy from the following list and discuss the advantages and disadvantages of its use versus that of fossil fuels: geothermal energy, solar energy, nuclear energy, wind energy, tidal energy, hydroelectric energy.

CHAPTER 23 : Critical Thinking

BREAKING A CIRCUIT

The circuit breaker illustrated and discussed in your text has a switch that includes a bimetallic strip. The circuit breaker shown here makes use of the magnetic field that is produced when a current flows through a wire. A coil of current-carrying wire that produces a magnetic field is called an electromagnet. In this circuit breaker, the electromagnet acts as a switch.

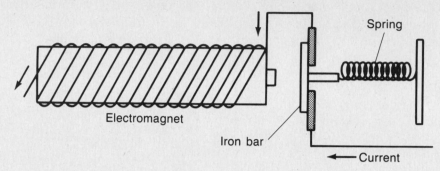

1. When current flows through the coil, the electromagnet exerts a force on the iron bar. The diagram shows another object that exerts a force on the iron bar. Identify that object.

2. What happens to the amount of current in a circuit as more and more appliances are in use in that circuit?

3. As the current increases, the strength of the magnetic field increases, and the iron bar is pulled to the electromagnet. How does this action open the circuit?

4. The circuit breaker shown in your text does not make use of an electromagnet. What effect of electric current is the basis for the bimetallic-strip circuit breaker shown in the text?

5. In what way are the two types of circuit breakers similar?

CHAPTER
24

Critical Thinking

THE DOORBELL

The diagram shows a doorbell that has an electromagnet as its main component.

1. Starting from the positive terminal of the battery, name the components of the circuit through which the electric current will pass when the doorbell rings.

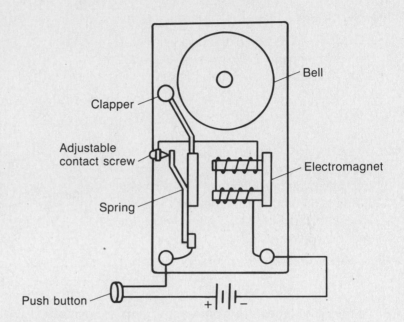

2. When the push button is used, a surge of current flows through the circuit. What effect does the electromagnet have on the spring and clapper assembly?

3. When the clapper hits the bell, the spring will no longer be touching the contact screw. What effect will this have on the flow of current and the electromagnet?

4. Why does the clapper keep hitting the bell repeatedly as long as the button is pushed?

5. Many doorbells have adjustable contact screws which can vary the distance between the spring and clapper assembly and the electromagnet. This permits the doorbell to function over a range of operating voltages. If a bell has been operating at 16 V and must now be used in a 12-V system, what changes would you make in the contact screw adjustment and explain why this is necessary?

6. What other electrical devices use the doorbell's system to rapidly switch an electromagnet on and off?

CHAPTER 25 : Critical Thinking

THE ELECTRIC GENERATOR

A generator contains an armature, which consists of a number of loops of wire wrapped around an iron core. The armature is spun in a magnetic field. In the diagram shown below, a single loop of wire represents a coil made up of many loops.

1. What is the direction of the magnetic field? To represent this field, draw a single arrow, labeled **M**, on the diagram.

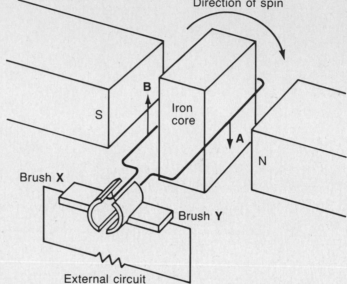

2. Since the armature is spinning clockwise, the section of the loop labeled **A** is moving downward through the magnetic field. Using a right-hand rule, determine if the *EMF* is toward or away from you in this section of the wire.

3. At the same time as section **A** of the loop is moving downward, section **B** is moving upward through the magnetic field. What is the direction of the *EMF* in section **B** of the loop? To show the direction of the current, draw arrows along sections **A** and **B** of the loop. Label these arrows **C**.

4. The loop is connected to the external circuit by a split-ring commutator, which is in contact with two brushes. Through which brush is current entering the external circuit?

5. After turning through one half of a rotation, section **A** of the loop will be moving upward and section **B** will be moving downward. What effect will this have on the direction of the current in the loop?

6. The one-half rotation puts loop section **A** in contact with brush **X**, and loop section **B** in contact with brush **Y**. What effect does this have on the direction of current in the external circuit?

7. A loop of current-carrying wire wrapped around an iron core forms an electromagnet. Use a right-hand rule to determine the N-pole and S-pole of the electromagnet formed by the spinning armature in the diagram. Label them **N** and **S**.

CHAPTER
26

Critical
Thinking

THE MICROWAVE OVEN

You have seen that a coil and a capacitor can be used to generate an oscillating field. However, there is a limit to the frequency of oscillation from such a unit. A device that produces a higher-frequency oscillation is the magnetron, which is the source of electromagnetic waves in a microwave oven. The magnetron consists of a central cathode surrounded by an anode block. The anode block contains a series of cavities, which function as resonating chambers. A strong magnet produces a magnetic field around the cathode and anode block. When electrons are emitted by the cathode, the magnetic field accelerates the electrons into a circular path. Electrons strike the openings to the cavities, and lose kinetic energy to the cavities, which oscillate. Meanwhile, the electrons return to the cathode. The frequency of the oscillation determines the frequency of the electromagnetic wave produced.

1. The walls of the resonating cavities develop a magnetic field, and the space between the walls develops an electric field. How is this similar to the coil-and-capacitor unit in an oscillator?

Anode block

Cavity resonators

Cathode

2. Why does the magnetron produce only one frequency of electromagnetic wave? How does this affect the amount of energy it can produce for heating food?

3. The variable power settings on a microwave oven do not change the energy output of the magnetron. Instead the magnetron is turned on and off at regular intervals. Boiling a cup of water at 50% power takes twice as long as it does at 100% power. Explain why.

4. If you have a microwave oven, you can determine the length of the on-and-off cycle that varies the power. Design a method to make this determination.

CHAPTER 27 : Critical Thinking

STEP BY STEP

You know that electrons orbit the nucleus of an atom. When an electron absorbs energy, it moves to another energy level, which is farther from the nucleus. According to quantum theory, an electron cannot absorb just any amount of energy, or move into just any energy level. The electron makes a "quantum leap." It cannot move only part of the way.

A staircase can give you an idea of how energy is quantized. Imagine a staircase in which each step is 0.20 m higher than the preceding step. You have a 0.50-kg block, which you can place on any step. The potential energy of the block can be calculated using the equation $PE = mgh$. The potential energy at the floor level is 0 because h is equal to 0.

1. To what energy level in an atom does the floor at the base of the stairs correspond? Explain your answer.

2. How much energy must you give the block to raise it from the floor to the first step?

3. How much energy must you give the block to raise it from the floor to the second step?

4. Suppose the block were on the floor and you increased its energy by 0.36 J. How high above the floor could you move the block?

5. Would this amount of energy raise the block to the next step? Explain your answer.

6. How is the staircase like the quantum model of the atom?

7. How is the staircase different from the quantum model of the atom?

CHAPTER
28

Critical Thinking

STAR SPECTRA

Spectrographic analysis is used by astronomers to determine the composition of stars. The spectrum of a star depends on the star's temperature and composition. No two stars have exactly the same spectrum. The top two spectra shown are star spectra. The other spectra were produced by individual elements.

1. What kind of spectra are the star spectra shown?

2. What kind of spectra are those shown for the elements?

3. Approximately what wavelengths are found on the hydrogen spectrum?

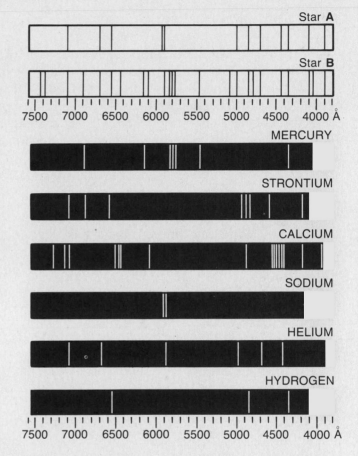

4. Does hydrogen occur in the atmosphere of star **A**? Of star **B**?

5. What is the atmospheric composition of star **A**?

6. What is the atmospheric composition of star **B**?

7. Which elements do not occur in the atmosphere of either star?

CHAPTER
29
Critical Thinking

REMOTE CONTROL

A wireless remote-control unit for a television set or a video recorder consists of a transmitter unit and a receiver unit. Each unit contains a diode and a microchip, as well as a source of current. Suppose you want to turn on the television. When you push the button on the transmitter, current flows to the microchip, or encoder. Here a series of electrical pulses are produced and sent to the diode. The pulses are in binary code, the "language" of computers and all chip-operated devices. The diode in the transmitter unit is a light-emitting diode, which produces flashes of infrared light in binary code. In the receiver unit, the flashes of infrared light strike a light-sensitive diode, called a photodiode. The photodiode produces electrical pulses in binary code. The microchip in this circuit serves as a decoder. After the signal is decoded, the receiver unit causes the correct change to occur in the television set. In this example, the current is turned on.

1. Why must you point the transmitter unit directly at the receiver unit?

2. Is the LED forward biased or reverse biased? Explain your answer.

3. Why are the pulses of light produced by the transmitter in the same coded form as the electrical pulses produced by the encoder?

4. The transmitter unit uses a battery as a source of current. When the batteries begin to wear out, the potential difference they create gradually decreases. What happens to the signal as the batteries begin to wear out? Explain your answer.

5. When light strikes the photodiode, electrons are removed from atoms. What is the name of this effect?

6. The removal of electrons from atoms in the photodiode increases the flow of current in the diode. Is this diode forward biased or reverse biased? Explain your answer.

CHAPTER
30 : Critical
Thinking

DISTANCE AND RADIOACTIVITY

Table 1 shows the results of an experiment in which radiation was detected by a Geiger-Mueller counter placed at various distances from a radioactive source. Before the radioactive source was brought in, the background level of radiation was found to be 41 counts per minute. The readings shown in Table 1 include the background count, and must be corrected before the data can be graphed.

Table 1

Distance (cm)	Activity (counts/min)	Corrected activity (counts/min)
4	745	
6	311	
8	217	
10	151	
12	111	
14	91	
16	85	

1. Prepare a graph of the corrected activity versus distance. What does the shape of the graph tell you about the relationship between measured activity and distance from the source?

2. If you wanted to produce a graph of a linear relationship, what variables would you compare?

3. Using the data provided, find the values you need to graph the relationship that will provide a straight-line graph. Add the new data to Table 1. Prepare your graph.

4. Use your second graph to predict the activity at a distance of 9 cm from the source. Is this the amount that would be detected by the Geiger-Mueller counter? Explain your answer.

31 Critical Thinking

THE PENETRATING POWER OF RADIATION

Different types of radiation differ in their abilities to penetrate matter. Alpha particles are the most easily blocked. One sheet of cardboard can be enough to block alpha radiation. Beta particles are more penetrating. Gamma rays are the most penetrating form of radiation.

In this exercise, you will analyze the results of a test of the effect of the thickness of the shielding material on the penetrating power of beta radiation. A source of beta radiation was placed near a Geiger-Mueller tube, and the activity was measured. Then sheets of shielding materials were placed between the source and the Geiger-Mueller tube. The distance between the source and the tube was kept constant. The results are recorded in Table 1. These data have been corrected for background radiation. Study the data and answer the questions that follow.

Table 1

Activity Measured Through Shielding (counts/min)								
Number of sheets	0	1	2	4	6	8	10	12	14
Cardboard	1000	756	633	444	311	217	152	106	75
Aluminum	1000	616	499	328	215	141	93	61	40
Lead	1000	518	355	110	45	10	1	—	—

1. What was the purpose of measuring the activity with no shielding material in place?

2. Why was it important to keep the distance between the source and the Geiger-Mueller tube constant?

3. What happened to the activity readings as more sheets of shielding materials were placed between the source and the Geiger-Mueller tube? How would you explain these data?

4. Which material was most effective in blocking radiation? What assumption must you make before using the data as a basis for your answer?

5. Prepare a graph of activity versus number of sheets of shielding material. What is the relationship between the thickness of the shielding material and the measured activity? Is the relationship linear?

6. If you wanted to know the shielding effect of two pieces of lead, but had only cardboard to use, how many pieces of cardboard would be needed?

CHAPTER 1
Critical Thinking

SUPERCONDUCTIVITY

Superconductors are materials that have no resistance to conducting an electrical current. Many materials become superconductors at very low temperatures. The temperature at which a material becomes a superconductor is called the *transition temperature*. The scale below shows the transition temperature for several substances.

1. What range of temperatures is shown on the scale?

   −273°C to −249°C

2. What is the value of absolute zero on the scale?

   −273°C

3. Estimate the transition temperature (to the nearest degree Celsius) of niobium nitride.

   −257°C

4. At what temperature does lead become a superconductor?

   −266°C

5. Which substance becomes a superconductor at a higher temperature, tin or niobium-tin?

   niobium-tin

6. Rank the following substances in order of decreasing transition temperature: vanadium, aluminum, technetium, and thallium.

   technetium, vanadium, thallium, aluminum

7. Which substance needs to be cooled the most to become a superconductor? What is its transition temperature?

   titanium; −273°C

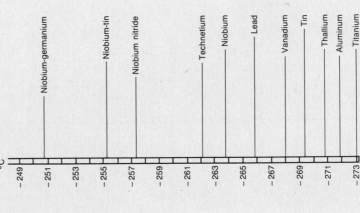

°C

−249	
−251	Niobium-germanium
−253	
−255	Niobium-tin
−257	Niobium nitride
−259	
−261	Technetium
−263	Niobium
−265	Lead
−267	Vanadium
−269	Tin
−271	Thallium
	Aluminum
−273	Titanium

CHAPTER 2
Critical Thinking

DIRECT AND INDIRECT MEASUREMENTS

Materials

100-mL graduated cylinder   vernier caliper or metric ruler
dried beans

Procedure

Use a vernier caliper or metric ruler to measure the thickness of three different beans. Record your data in Table 1 and find the average thickness. Use a graduated cylinder to measure the volume of some beans. Then spread the beans in a single layer on a tabletop, and arrange the beans so that they form the smallest possible circle. You have formed a cylinder with a height equal to the thickness of one bean. Measure the diameter of this cylinder. Repeat this procedure twice, using different numbers of beans each time. Record your data in Table 2. The equation for the volume of a cylinder is $V = \pi r^2 h$. Solve the equation for h, and find the average value.

Results

Table 1

Sample data are given.

Bean	h (cm)
1	0.15
2	0.19
3	0.17
Average	0.17

Table 2

Trial	Volume (cm³)	Diameter (cm)	Radius (cm)	h (cm)
1	95	28	14	0.15
2	93	28	14	0.15
3	85	26	13	0.16
Average				0.15

1. Which measurement is a direct measurement?

   Using the vernier caliper or metric ruler gives a direct measurement.

CHAPTER 2 Critical Thinking

2. Which measurement is an indirect measurement?

Calculating the thickness from volume measurements is an indirect measurement.

3. Which method gives the more accurate measurement of the thickness of a bean?

The direct method is more accurate.

4. What are some sources of error in making the indirect measurement? How might these sources of error be reduced?

Sources of error include using beans of varying thickness, the air spaces between beans in the graduated cylinder, gaps between beans in the circle on the table, and arranging the beans in a shape that is not exactly circular. These sources of error can be reduced if a uniform selection of beans can be obtained, and if care is taken to minimize air spaces and distortions of the circle.

5. When might indirect measurements be useful? Give an example.

Indirect measurements are useful when it is difficult to make a direct measurement. Examples might include measurements of Earth's dimensions or distances in space.

CHAPTER 3 Critical Thinking

POSITIONS ALONG A ROLLER COASTER

You have seen position-time graphs that illustrate movement in one direction. But how would you diagram movement in more than one direction, as in a roller coaster? The position-time information shown is for a trip on a very small roller coaster. The position information describes horizontal movement along the ground and vertical movement up in the air.

Time (s)	Horizontal Position (m)	Vertical Position (m)
1	0	11
2	1	11
3	2	11
4	4	8
5	7	5
6	11	1
7	17	0
8	21	2
9	22	5
10	21	8
11	17	10
12	13	8
13	12	5
14	13	2
15	17	0
16	21	0
17	24	0
18	27	3
19	29	5
20	31	7
21	33	7
22	35	5
23	38	2
24	40	0

1. Using graph paper, plot a position-time graph for the movement along the ground. Describe the curve.

It rises, falls, and rises again.

2. Is the velocity constant?

No.

3. Describe the velocity at 9 seconds and at 13 seconds.

At 9 seconds, the velocity changes direction and becomes negative. At 13 seconds, it becomes positive again.

NAME _____

Horizontal Distance vs Time

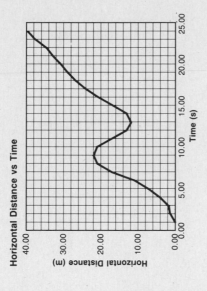

Vertical Distance vs Time

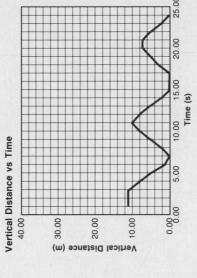

Vertical Distance vs Horizontal Distance

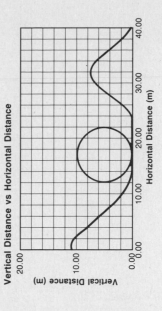

4. What would you see if you were in a balloon above the roller coaster and could not see any vertical movement, only movement along the round?

   You would see the car move forward, then backward at 9 seconds, then forward at 13.

5. Using another sheet of graph paper, plot a position-time graph for the vertical movement. Describe the curve.

   It falls, rises, falls again, rises again, and falls a third time.

6. Is this velocity constant?

   No.

7. How would you describe this motion?

   up and down movement in several waves

8. If you were standing at the very end of the roller coaster, watching as the car came straight toward you, what kind of movement would you see?

   You would see the car fall and rise twice, and then fall.

9. Using a third sheet of graph paper, plot the position along the ground against the position above the ground. Use the same scale on each axis, and plot the distance along the ground as the x-axis. This graph will represent the position of the car at each point in time. After you have plotted the points, connect them in the correct time sequence. What does the shape of the graph represent?

   the shape of the roller coaster

10. Describe the shape of the roller coaster.

    an initial slope down, a circular loop, and a final hill

11. Now that you know the shape of the roller coaster, what was happening between 7 and 15 seconds? Between 17 and 24 seconds?

    Between 7 and 15 seconds, the roller coaster car was going around the loop, and between 17 and 24 seconds, it was going over the hill.

CHAPTER 4 : Critical Thinking

ACCELERATION AND ESCAPE VELOCITY

During the twenty-first century, journeys may be made to and from Mars. In the years that follow, other objects in the solar system may become the targets for round-trip explorations by spacecraft. Many obstacles will have to be overcome to achieve successful round trips. One of the most formidable of these will be to accelerate the spacecraft to the velocity required for them to escape the gravitational attraction of the object on which they have landed. This value, called *escape velocity*, must be reached in a reasonable amount of time. For the purposes of this activity, assume that the required time is 1000 seconds.

Based on the above criterion and the data in the table below, answer the questions that follow.

Table 1

Object	Velocity (km/s)	Acceleration required (km/s²)
Mercury	4.2	0.0042
Venus	10.0	0.01
Mars	5.0	0.005
Earth	11.3	0.0113
Moon	2.4	0.0024
Jupiter	59.7	0.0597
Saturn	35.4	0.0354
Uranus	24.1	0.0241
Neptune	24.1	0.0241

1. Assuming that the masses of all space-craft are equal, predict from which object escape would be most difficult. From which object would escape be least difficult?

   It would be most difficult to escape from Jupiter and least difficult to escape from the moon.

2. If the rockets used to boost the space-craft from each of these objects produced constant acceleration, what would be the shape of the curve on a velocity-time graph in each case?

   The curve would be a straight line.

3. Which curve would have the greatest slope?

   The curve for Jupiter would have the greatest slope.

4. Calculate the constant acceleration required to reach each escape velocity in 1000.0 s. Show your calculations.

   $a = v/t$
   = $\frac{4.2 \text{ m/s}}{1000.0 \text{ s}}$
   = 0.0042 km/s²

5. Is your prediction in Question 1 supported? Explain your answer.

   Answer will vary depending on whether the prediction was correct. Escape would be most difficult from the object requiring the greatest acceleration (Jupiter).

6. Based on your observations from films or videos of space flights, how do you think achievement of escape velocity in such flights differs from that assumed in Question 2?

   In real space flights, variable acceleration rather than constant acceleration is used to achieve escape velocity.

CHAPTER 5 : Critical Thinking

FORCES AND FLIGHT

The four forces that act on an airplane in flight are thrust, drag, lift, and weight. When the propellers of the airplane turn, they exert a force that pushes air backward. The air exerts an equal force on the propellers, forcing them, and the airplane, forward. This forward force is thrust. Drag is caused by the air. As the airplane moves forward, this force acts in a backward direction. Lift is an upward force caused by the movement of air over the wings of the airplane. The amount of lift is related to the shape of the wing and the forward velocity of the airplane. The faster the airplane moves, the greater the lift force. Weight is a downward force caused by gravity. The greater the mass of the airplane and its contents, the greater the downward force.

1. Which of the forces described form a pair of action-reaction forces? Which of Newton's laws describes such a pair of forces?

   The force of the moving propellers on the air and the force of the air on the propellers are action-reaction forces. Newton's third law describes such pairs.

2. Which two forces must be balanced if the airplane is to fly at a constant forward velocity? Which of Newton's laws describes such balanced forces?

   The forward force, thrust, and the backward force, drag, must be balanced if the plane is to fly at a constant forward velocity. Newton's first law describes balanced forces.

3. Which two forces must be balanced if the airplane is to fly at a constant altitude?

   The upward force, lift, and the downward force, weight, must be balanced if the plane is to fly at a constant altitude.

4. To take off, an airplane must accelerate until its forward velocity gives it enough lift to get off the ground. What are two ways in which the mass of the airplane affects takeoff?

   The mass of the airplane gives it weight, which opposes the upward force of lift. The greater the weight, the more lift is needed to take off. The mass of the airplane also affects its ability to accelerate. The greater the mass of the airplane, the more thrust, or forward force, needed to accelerate the airplane to takeoff velocity.

5. Flaps on the airplane wings can be moved to change the shape of the wings. During landing, the flaps decrease lift and increase drag. How do these changes help the airplane to land?

   Decreasing lift causes downward acceleration of the airplane, moving it closer to the ground. Increasing drag decreases the forward velocity. This helps the airplane to come to a stop after landing. It also reduces lift, because lift depends on forward motion.

6. As the airplane moves through the air, two factors cause drag. What are they? Why do they cause drag to be greater at lower altitudes?

   The two factors are friction between molecules in the air, and the resistance of the air to something that moves through it. These factors are greater at low altitudes because air is denser, and the molecules in air are closer together.

DATE ———— PERIOD ———— NAME ————

CHAPTER 6 Critical Thinking

MEASURING HEIGHT INDIRECTLY

Materials

string
protractor
meter stick
tape
metric tape measure
large-diameter drinking straw
washer or other weight

Procedure

Work with a partner. Hold a meter stick on end so that it is perpendicular to the floor. You may wish to tape or clamp the meter stick to an upright support. Hold one end of a piece of string on the top of the meter stick, and have your partner extend the string to the floor in front of the meter stick. The string should be held as taut as possible. Your partner will measure the angle between the floor and the string, the distance along the floor from the meter stick to the point where the string touches the floor, and the length of the string. Record these measurements in Table 1. Use your data to calculate the height of the meter stick. There are three different methods to use. Compare your calculations with the known height of the meter stick.

Make a clinometer like the one shown in the drawing. Tape a protractor to a drinking straw so that the straw is at a right angle to the base of the protractor. Tape a weighted string to the protractor. Be sure that the string can swing freely. When you look through the straw at an object, the position of the string against the protractor will show the angle between your line of sight and the horizontal. CAUTION: *Never look at the sun or any other bright object through the clinometer.*

Using your clinometer and a tape measure, you can indirectly measure the height of objects such as buildings or trees. Devise a procedure to make indirect measurements. Test your procedure by calculating the height of a structure of known height, such as the school building or a flagpole.

8   CRITICAL THINKING

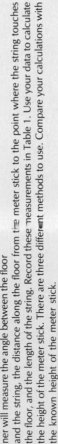

Protractor

Drinking straw

25°

Washer

DATE ———— NAME ————

CHAPTER 6 Critical Thinking

Results

Table 1

Length of string (m) _____

Distance along floor (m) _____

Angle _____

Height (use angle and length of string) _____

Height (use angle and distance along floor) (m) _____

Height (use Pythagorean theorem) (m) _____

Height (known value) (m) _____

1. List the steps of your method for using a clinometer.

   Measure the angle to the top of the chosen structure. Measure the distance from the structure to the observer. Use tan θ = opposite/adjacent to calculate the height of the structure. Add the height of the observer's eyes.

2. Why is this method more practical than the string method?

   While it might be possible to stretch a string from the top of a low building to the ground, it would not be safe or practical to stretch a string from the top of a tree or a tall building to the ground.

3. Notice that Table 2 includes a column headed "Corrected height." What measurement must be added to the calculated height? How could you avoid having to make this correction?

   The height of the observer's eyes must be added. To avoid making this correction, lie on the ground to measure the angle.

Table 2

Object	Distance (m)	Angle	Height (m)	Corrected height (m)

CRITICAL THINKING   9

CHAPTER 7 Critical Thinking

MECHANICAL RESONANCE

Materials

two vertical lab supports or ring stands
string
two weights

Procedure

If you suspend a weight from a string and push on the weight, it will swing back and forth in simple harmonic motion. If you want to increase the amplitude of the swing, you can do so by pushing on the swinging weight at a specific time in its swing. This effect is known as mechanical resonance. To investigate this effect, tie a string between two vertical supports, and then use a second piece of string and a weight to form a pendulum that hangs from the string. Set the pendulum in motion and observe its behavior. Try to increase the amplitude of the pendulum by applying a small force at regular intervals of time.

Use another piece of string and a second weight to suspend another pendulum from the horizontal string. The two pendulums should be the same length. Start only one pendulum moving and note what happens. Try this again, but vary the length of one of the pendulums.

Results

1. When you had only one pendulum set up, what was the best time in its motion to add the extra force?

The best time to add more force is when the pendulum is at the highest point in its swing, and is just about to move downward.

2. Describe what happened when you had two pendulums of identical length, and started one moving.

The moving pendulum gradually moves with a smaller amplitude as the second pendulum begins to move. Eventually the original pendulum has almost no amplitude in its swing and the second pendulum has the large amplitude. Then the situation reverses, and the original pendulum has the larger amplitude, and the second pendulum has almost no amplitude. This reversing continues until the pendulums stop moving.

3. What caused the resonance effect you saw?

As the first pendulum was swinging it caused the horizontal string to vibrate at the same frequency. Because this is also the natural frequency of the second pendulum, resonance caused the second pendulum to move. As it moved more, and had more energy, the first pendulum lost energy. The energy was transferred back and forth between the two pendulums, causing them to vary in amplitude.

4. Could you get the same effect when the pendulums were of different lengths? Explain your answer.

The effect only occurs when the two pendulums have the same length and the same natural frequency. With pendulums of different lengths, the pendulum may move a little from time to time, but it never develops a full-amplitude swing.

5. In all cases, the pendulums eventually stop moving. Why?

The pendulums stop swinging because of air resistance, which causes them to lose energy.

CHAPTER 8 Critical Thinking

ACCELERATION DUE TO GRAVITY

Isaac Newton made a number of contributions to our knowledge of gravitation and the variables that account for its effects. Table 1 contains data about the sun and the nine planets of the solar system. Analyze the data carefully. To help you do this, complete Table 2. Then answer the questions that follow.

Table 1

Object	Mass (kg)	Acceleration due to gravity (m/s²)
Sun	1.991×10^{30}	293.0
Mercury	3.2×10^{23}	3.72
Venus	4.88×10^{24}	8.82
Earth	5.979×10^{21}	9.80
Mars	6.42×10^{23}	3.72
Jupiter	1.901×10^{27}	24.8
Saturn	5.68×10^{26}	10.5
Uranus	8.68×10^{25}	9.01
Neptune	1.03×10^{26}	11.7
Pluto	1.15×10^{22}	0.49

Table 2

Object (in order of decreasing mass)	Object (in order of decreasing acceleration due to gravity)
Sun	Sun
Jupiter	Jupiter
Saturn	Neptune
Neptune	Saturn
Uranus	Earth
Earth	Uranus
Venus	Venus
Mars	Mars
Mercury	Mercury
Pluto	Pluto

1. Based on the data, what generalization seems most appropriate?

Although there are apparent exceptions, the data tend to support the generalization that acceleration due to gravity varies directly with the mass of the object.

2. Are there exceptions to the generalization?

Yes. Saturn and Neptune are in reverse order as are Earth and Uranus.

3. If there are exceptions in Question 2, how might you account for these?

Since acceleration due to gravity is measured at the surface of an object and since gravity increases exponentially as the distance between the surface of an object and its center decreases, an object of lesser mass but smaller radius may possess a greater acceleration due to gravity than an object of greater mass and greater radius. Table 8-1 in the student text reveals that the radius of Neptune is indeed less than half that of Saturn and the radius of Earth is about one-quarter that of Uranus. Thus, it is reasonable to conclude that the radii of these objects account for what at first glance appear to be exceptions to the rule.

4. In what way would your weight vary, if at all, if you were to find yourself on each of the objects represented in the table? Explain your answe

   Your weight would decrease as you moved down the objects in the order listed in the second column of Table 2. Weight is a measure of force that varies directly with acceleration due to gravity.

5. From which object would the least energy be required to launch a projectile into space? Explain your answer.

   Pluto. Since Pluto possesses the lowest acceleration due to gravity, thus the lowest force of attraction to its surface, less energy would be required to overcome that force than would be the case on any of the other objects.

HIGHWAY BARRIERS

Anyone who has driven down a major highway on a long journey has encountered places where relatively sudden forks in the highway demand quick decisions. Highway safety experts know that drivers approaching such a fork at high speed have become confused, lost control of their vehicle, and plowed into the apex of the concrete divider which separates the diverging roads. The result has often been a serious or deadly accident.

Since the advent of freeways, superhighways, and other high-speed roads, safety engineers have tried to improve the safety of road travel by doing such things as improving lighting and road signs. Nevertheless, drivers still got confused and found themselves hurtling toward a virtually immovable concrete barrier and certain injury or death. Another solution had to be invented—and it was. The invention, a series of cans filled with sand and placed in front of the concrete barrier, was the idea of a former race car driver named John Fitch. Appropriately, the arrays of such cans are called "Fitch Inertial Barriers." In this exercise, you will explore practical applications of Fitch's invention. Assume that the only variable in the construction of the automobiles in the table is mass and that the occupants of the cars are of equal mass.

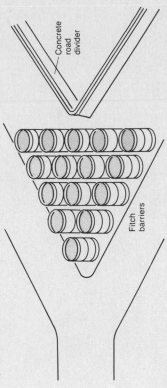

Concrete road divider

Fitch barriers

Table 1

Automobile	Mass (kg)	Velocity (km/h)
1	910	82
2	1675	29
3	1200	50
4	1350	63
5	1500	40

1. What general principle accounts for the safety features of the Fitch barriers?

   Fitch barriers increase the time during which the force of a collision is exerted on a vehicle and its occupants. Since the total force of the collision is a constant, spreading it out over time reduces the force applied to the car and its occupants during the duration of the collision.

CHAPTER
10 Critical Thinking

BICYCLE GEARS

Materials

ten-speed bicycle

Procedure

On a ten-speed bicycle, there are two gears at the pedals and five at the rear wheel, producing ten different combinations, or gear ratios. To see how the gears work, turn the bicycle upside down. Turn the pedal and count the number of times the rear wheel turns for each turn of the pedal. Try this in first, fifth, and tenth gears, and note which combination of front and rear gears is in use.

Count the teeth on each of the front gears and record these data in Table 1. Count the teeth on each of the rear gears and record these data. Calculate the ratio of the number of teeth on the front gear to the number of teeth on the rear gear.

Results

Table 1   Sample data are given.

Gear	Front		Rear				
	Large	Small	A (largest)	B	C	D	E (smallest)
Number of teeth	52	40	28	24	20	17	14
Ratio with large gear			1.86	2.17	2.60	3.06	3.71
Ratio with small gear			1.43	1.67	2.00	2.35	2.86

1. How does the force on the pedal vary in first, fifth, and tenth gears?
The least amount of force is needed in first gear. More force is needed in fifth gear. Tenth gear requires the most force.

2. How many revolutions of the rear wheel were there for one revolution of the pedals in first, fifth, and tenth gears? How does the ratio of revolutions compare to the gear ratios?
Answers will vary, depending on the bicycle used, but in first gear there will be between 1 and 1.5 wheel revolutions. In fifth gear, there will be between 2 and 2.3 wheel revolutions. In tenth gear, there will be between 3.5 and 4 wheel revolutions.

3. What gear combination would you use to climb hills? Explain your answer.
To climb hills, use the lowest gear ratio because this ratio requires the least force on the pedals.

4. What gear combination would you use to maintain a high speed on a flat, level road? Explain your answer.
To maintain speed on a level road, use the highest gear ratio, because this produces the largest number of wheel revolutions for each revolution of the pedals.

5. A machine can multiply force or speed, but not both. Explain how the bicycle demonstrates this statement.
The bicycle is a machine designed to multiply speed. Even in first gear, the rear wheel makes more revolutions than the pedals. The gears multiply speed at a cost. The greater the multiplication of speed, as in higher gears, the greater the amount of force that must be applied to the pedals.

CHAPTER
9 Critical Thinking

2. Which automobile will penetrate most deeply into the array of Fitch barriers? Explain your answers.

Automobile 4 possesses the greatest momentum. Since the distance of penetration is directly proportional to momentum, automobile 4 will penetrate most deeply.

3. Which automobile will penetrate least deeply into the array of Fitch barriers? Explain your answer.

Automobile 2 possesses the least momentum, so it will penetrate least deeply.

4. Considering only automobiles 3 and 5, the occupants of which of these cars are least likely to sustain serious injuries? Explain your answers.

People in automobile 5 are the least likely to be seriously injured. Since both cars have the same momentum they will penetrate the Fitch barriers to the same depth in the same amount of time. However, since the velocity on initial impact is less for automobile 5 (40 km/h) than it is for automobile 3 (50 km/h), the negative acceleration for the occupants of automobile 5 will be less than for the occupants of automobile 3.

5. If the Fitch barriers were absent, the occupants of which car would be most likely to sustain serious injuries? Assume the concrete divider is an immovable object. Explain your answer.

Without Fitch barriers, the people in automobile 1 would have the most serious injuries. Since all the automobiles would come to an abrupt stop, that is, their velocity would instantly become zero, any loose objects in the cars would strike hard surfaces in proportion to the automobile's velocity. Since automobile 1's velocity is the greatest, its occupants would most likely sustain the greatest injuries.

6. If the Fitch barriers were absent, the occupants of which automobile would be least likely to sustain serious injuries? Explain your answer.

Since the velocity of automobile 2 is the least, its occupants would likely sustain the most minor injuries.

CHAPTER
11 : Critical : Thinking

ENDLESS ENERGY?

You know that energy is conserved. You have seen examples of energy changing from one form to another in a seemingly endless chain. If that is true, can someone make a machine that could go on forever? Throughout history, people have dreamed of a machine like this. Once you put energy in, the machine would run itself. It would be like getting something for nothing!

The diagram shows a sixteenth-century design for a "perpetual motion" water pump. The diagonal part is based on an ancient device that actually did work. It had a spiral channel that filled with water when the screw was turned. The perpetual motion version of the pump was supposed to eliminate the work of turning the screw. The sixteenth-century inventor added a series of tiny paddles. When water falling from the top of the screw hit the paddles, it would power the pump. Look closely at the diagram, and think about it in terms of energy.

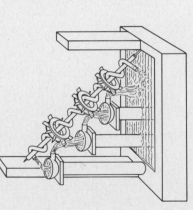

1. What form of energy has the water gained on reaching the top of the spiral?

   The water has potential energy.

2. What kind of energy would the water have when it falls onto the paddles? What does this energy do next?

   The water has kinetic energy. It turns the screws.

3. What could cause this device to run out of energy? Where does the energy go?

   Energy is not lost. It may only seem to get lost. Friction causes some of the kinetic energy to be changed into heat energy. The heat leaves the system and does not contribute to useful work.

4. Dream up a perpetual motion machine that you yourself could use. First, decide what you want the machine to do. Make a simple diagram of your idea.

   Encourage students to be creative and to think of modern versions of perpetual motion machines.

CHAPTER
12 : Critical : Thinking

COMPARING HEAT ENGINES

In your text you have seen a diagram of an automobile's gasoline engine. This engine is called a four-stroke engine because there are four strokes, or movements, of the piston in each fuel-burning cycle. The diesel engine, shown in the diagram on this page, is another kind of four-stroke engine. The greatest difference between the diesel engine and the gasoline engine is that the diesel engine does not use a spark plug to ignite the fuel. The air in the cylinder is compressed so much that when the fuel enters the cylinder, the high temperature of the air causes the fuel to ignite spontaneously. The diesel engine does not burn gasoline. Instead it burns diesel fuel, which is a less refined hydrocarbon.

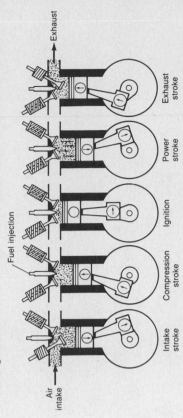

Air intake

Fuel injection

Exhaust

Intake stroke   Compression stroke   Ignition   Power stroke   Exhaust stroke

1. In the first stroke of a gasoline engine, a mixture of gasoline and air enters the cylinder. This mixture is controlled by a device called a carburetor. How is the first stroke in a diesel engine different?

   In the first stroke of the diesel engine, only air is taken into the cylinder.

2. Does a diesel engine need a carburetor? Explain your answer.

   A diesel engine does not need a carburetor, because air and fuel are not mixed until they enter the cylinder.

3. In the second stroke of each engine, the contents of the cylinder are compressed. What else happens during the compression stroke in the diesel engine?

   Fuel is injected into the cylinder.

4. What energy change takes place during the third stroke in each engine?

   As the fuel burns, the gases in the cylinder expand, and push on the piston. Thermal energy is changed into mechanical energy.

5. What happens during the fourth stroke in the diesel engine? How does this compare with the fourth stroke in the gasoline engine?

   In the fourth stroke, exhaust gases are pushed out of the cylinder. This is the same in both engines.

CHAPTER 12 Critical Thinking

6. Why would a diesel engine be less expensive to run than a gasoline engine?

   Diesel fuel is less refined, so it is cheaper to produce.

7. A diesel engine is heavier than a gasoline engine of comparable size. Explain why.

   The gases in the cylinders are compressed more than in a gasoline engine. The engine would have to be sturdier to withstand the greater pressure.

8. Although diesel engines are heavier than gasoline engines, they are more efficient. This trade-off makes them a good choice for trucks and locomotives. Explain why.

   A truck or a locomotive is so heavy that the extra weight of the engine is unimportant. The increased efficiency of the diesel engine is worth the minor increase in weight.

9. Sometimes the cylinders of a gasoline engine fire just after the ignition is turned off. This post-ignition spark is sometimes referred to as "dieseling." Explain why this term is appropriate.

   If there is some gasoline left in a cylinder, it may burn even though the spark plug is not causing ignition. Ignition without a spark is what happens normally in a diesel engine, so this comparison is appropriate.

CHAPTER 13 Critical Thinking

THE EFFECT OF THERMAL EXPANSION ON LAKES

Most liquids expand as they are heated and contract as they are cooled. As a result, a liquid is densest just before it freezes. Water is an exception to this rule, reaching a maximum density at 4°C. Because water at its freezing point is less dense than water between 0°C and 4°C, lakes freeze at the top. In most areas with a moderate climate, lakes do not freeze all the way to the bottom, and water at the bottom of the lake is a few degrees warmer than the ice at the top. Because water at each temperature has a different density, the lake develops layers of water.

When spring arrives, the ice melts and the water begins to warm. The water at the top of the lake warms first. When it reaches 4°C, the water falls to the bottom, creating a convection current. The lake is said to "turn over." This spring turnover is important for the organisms living in the lake. As the water moves, nutrients that have settled to the bottom become mixed into the water and become available to the organisms in the water. Also, oxygen from the air enters the surface water and is carried to the bottom of the lake as the lake turns over.

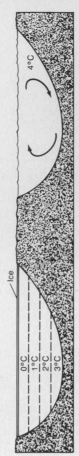

1. The drawing at the left shows the lake in winter. What is the temperature of the water just below the ice? What is the temperature at the bottom?

   The water just below the ice is at 0°C. The water at the bottom is at 3°C.

2. The drawing at the right shows the lake during the spring turnover. Describe the temperature distribution of the lake during the turnover.

   The temperature throughout the lake is 4°C. This occurs because the lake is being mixed.

3. As summer approaches, the lake again forms a layered pattern of temperature distribution. What are the main sources of heat for the lake? What part of the lake warms first?

   The sources of heat are the sun and the warm air above the water. The top of the lake warms first.

4. When the summer layers have formed, water temperatures may range from 12°C to 24°C. Where will the densest water be? Where will the warmest water be? Where will the coolest water be?

   The densest water will be at the bottom. The warmest water will be at the top. The coolest water, which is the densest, will be at the bottom.

5. In the late fall a second turnover takes place. What one condition must exist for the turnover to occur? What causes this condition?

   The water at the top of the lake must be so cool (usually 4°C) that it is denser than the rest of the water in the lake. This denser water will sink to the bottom, and start currents in the lake. Heat is lost from the lake to the cool air, which lowers the temperature of the lake.

CHAPTER 14
Critical Thinking

WAVE SUPERPOSITION

The diagram shows two periodic transverse waves traveling along a taut string in the same direction at the same time. According to the principle of superposition, interference between these two waves will produce a resultant wave. Study the diagram and compare the two waves. Look for points where maximum constructive interference would occur. Also look for points where maximum destructive interference would occur.

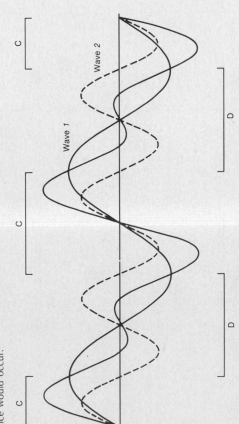

1. Which of the two waves has the greater amplitude?

   Wave 1 has the greater amplitude.

2. If the frequency of wave 1 is f_1 and the frequency of wave 2 is f_2, state the numerical relationship between the frequencies in the form of an equation.

   $f_2 = 2f_1$

3. If the wavelength of wave 1 is λ_1 and the wavelength of wave 2 is λ_2, state the numerical relationship between the wavelengths in the form of an equation.

   $\lambda_1 = 2\lambda_2$

4. State the principle of superposition. On the figure, sketch the resultant wave produced by the superposition of the two waves. Then label with a "C" the parts of the wave produced by constructive interference and with a "D" the parts of the wave produced by destructive interference.

   The displacement of a medium caused by two or more waves is the algebraic sum of the displacements caused by the individual waves.

CHAPTER 15
Critical Thinking

TUNING A GUITAR

Materials

guitar

Procedure

When a guitar is tuned, the musician begins with the top string, which is the thickest, and plays the lowest note. By holding the string against one of the small ridges, or frets, on the neck of the guitar, the musician raises the pitch of the sound made by the string. The thickest string is held against the fifth fret, and the next string is tightened or loosened until its pitch matches the thickest string. Each string is tuned in a similar manner, until the last string is in tune.

Beats are variations in amplitude caused by two sounds of close, but not identical, frequency. Listening for beats is a way to tell if two guitar strings are in tune. Start with a properly tuned guitar, and use the first and second strings. Hold the first string against the fifth fret, and then pluck both the first and second strings. They should play the same note. Try this again, and while the strings are vibrating, change the tension of the second string, and listen for beats.

Results

1. Do you hear beats when the two strings are properly in tune? Explain your answer.

   No, there are no beats because the two strings produce the same frequency.

2. What happens to the frequency of the beats as you adjust the second string further out of tune?

   The number of beats per second increases as the difference in frequency increases. When the number of beats per second becomes great enough, individual beats can no longer be detected.

3. Do the number of beats tell you if the pitch of the second string is higher or lower than the pitch of the first string?

   No, the number of beats only tells the frequency difference between the two strings. It does not tell which string has the higher pitch (frequency).

4. Re-tune the guitar, hold the first string against the fifth fret and pluck it. Then quickly stop its vibration. Explain what you hear after the vibration of the first string is stopped.

   The second string vibrates, although it was not plucked. This occurs when the two strings have the same natural frequency, and is called resonance.

5. Repeat the procedure in Question 4, but hold the first string at the fourth fret. Do you hear the same effect? Explain your answer.

   Resonance does not occur now because the second string is tuned to match the sound of the first string when it is held at the fifth fret. At the fourth fret, the first string vibrates at a different frequency, and resonance does not occur.

6. How can beats and resonance be used to find out if a guitar is in tune?

   When two strings made to play the same note are in tune, they will not produce beats. When one of the strings is plucked and then silenced, the other string will vibrate only if it is properly in tune.

CHAPTER 16 Critical Thinking

USING LIGHT TO ESTIMATE DISTANCE

Imagine that you have taken a camping trip to the Rocky Mountains with five friends. On a quiet evening when there seems to be nothing exciting to do, you decide to perform a seemingly impossible feat. You announce the following to your friends.

"I will climb that mountain five miles to the north taking with me only a pad of paper, a pencil, and a super-sensitive light meter that measures illuminance. Here are five identical flashlights. Beginning at 11:00 PM you may walk, jog, or run directly toward or away from me for one hour, or you may stay where you are. At midnight, stand still and shine the flashlights at me for a few seconds. Resume walking, jogging, running, or standing still for another hour till 1:00 AM. Flash your lights at me again. Then repeat the whole procedure for one more hour. I only ask that you line up from left to right and keep these relative positions so I can identify you by assigning you code numbers from 1 to 6. I'll come back to camp shortly after 2:00 AM and you can ask me questions about your activities between midnight and 2:00 AM. And I will answer every question correctly."

You head for the mountain, climb to the top, and over the next few hours collect the data shown. What are your answers to your friends' questions? Explain each answer.

Table 1

Friend	ILLUMINANCE (lm/m²)		
	Midnight	1:00 AM	2:00 AM
1	16	16	16
2	4	9	16
3	4	9	9
4	1	1	4
5	36	4	9

1. At midnight, which of us was closest to you?

   5 was the friend whose flashlight produced the greatest illuminance.

2. At midnight, which of us was farthest from you?

   4 was the friend whose flashlight produced the least illuminance.

3. From midnight to 2:00 AM, one of us did not appear to move. Which one?

   1 was the only friend whose flashlight produced the same illuminance at all three times.

4. From midnight to 1:00 AM, which of us traveled the greatest distance?

5. Based on the illuminance produced, and the inverse square rule, this friend increased the distance from the mountain by a factor of 3 (illuminance decreased by a factor of 9). No other friend has either increased or decreased his or her distance by so large a factor.

5. Which of us appeared to move continuously between midnight and 2:00 AM?

   2, 5. The illuminance of each of these friend's flashlight changes with each succeeding hour, which implies continuous motion.

6. Which of us appeared to be in continuous motion *towards* you?

   2. The illuminance of this friend's flashlight increased steadily from midnight to 2:00 AM, which implies that the friend was moving nearer.

CHAPTER 17 Critical Thinking

THE SHAPE OF A DIAMOND

The brilliance of a diamond depends on a number of factors. Among these is the way light is reflected and refracted by the diamond. If light were completely reflected by the surface of a diamond, it would simply act as a mirror and would be of no value as a gem. By the same token if light, once entering a diamond, were to be reflected endlessly within the diamond or escape from its bottom or lower sides, the diamond would also be of little value as a gem. Knowing this, a diamond cutter must produce a stone with 58 facets—or exterior surface planes—that form precise angles with one another. The cutter does this in such a way that the maximum amount of light entering the diamond leaves the facets near the top of the gem.

Based on the fact that the index of refraction of a diamond is 2.42, examine the following three simplified drawings of cut diamonds and answer the questions that follow. The only tool you will need is a protractor.

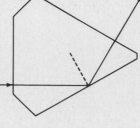

Light

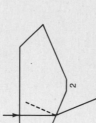

1

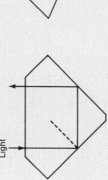

2

3

----- Normal

1. What datum must you first calculate?

   The critical angle of diamond.

2. How can you accomplish this calculation?

   By using the formula: $\sin \theta_c = 1/n$ in which n is the index of refraction for diamond and θ_c is its critical angle.

3. What is the numerical value of this datum?

   24.4°

4. Which of the diamonds is most correctly cut? Explain your answer.

   Diamond 1 is cut correctly. The cuts of the other two diamonds produce reflection that ultimately directs light out of the upper surface of the diamond.

5. To support your answer, complete each illustration by drawing its ray diagram.

CHAPTER 18 Critical Thinking

REFLECTING TELESCOPES

Various optical instruments have been invented to make distant objects appear nearer and larger than they actually are. Among these are a variety of telescopes and binoculars. Some consist solely of lenses while others combine lenses and mirrors. Two different kinds of reflecting telescopes are shown. How do they work? To find the answers, complete each ray diagram. Then answer the questions that follow.

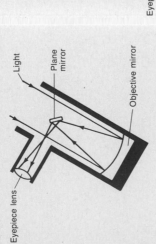

Newtonian Reflecting Telescope

Cassegrainian Reflecting Telescope

1. Why would these telescopes be impractical to view objects on Earth?

   Since they produce inverted images, objects viewed through them would appear upside down.

2. How does the size of the objective mirror affect the performance of these telescopes?

   The primary function of the objective mirror is to gather light emitted or reflected from a distant object. Therefore, the larger the mirror the more able it is to produce images of faint objects or objects removed from Earth by great distances. Put another way, telescopes with large objective mirrors can "see" further into space than can telescopes with small objective mirrors.

3. What components of the telescope determine the magnification? Explain your answer.

   Magnification is caused primarily by the eyepiece lens and the objective mirror. Magnification is determined by dividing the focal length of the objective by that of the eyepiece.

CHAPTER 19 Critical Thinking

DIFFRACTION

Materials

2 single-edged razor blades
straight filament lamp (showcase lamp)
cardboard
tape
thread
colored filters (red, green or blue cellophane or spotlight gelatin)

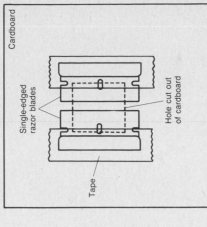

Procedure

Cut out a 2 cm × 2 cm square hole in a small sheet of cardboard. Tape the razor blades over the hole as shown. CAUTION: *Handle the razor blades with extreme care.* While holding the cardboard so the slit is vertical, stand 1–2 m from the lamp and observe the illuminated lamp through the slit. Repeat the procedure covering the slit in turn with various colored filters.

Next, place a length of thread vertically between the edges of the razor blades and tape the ends of the thread to the cardboard. The space between the razor blades should now be a double slit. Observe the lamp through the double slit. Repeat your observation with various colored filters covering the slit.

Results

1. Describe what you saw when looking at the lamp through a single slit with no colored filters. Describe what you saw when looking at the lamp through a single slit covered with colored filters.

   With no filter, there is a pattern that includes all the colors of the spectrum extending out from a central white area. With a filter, there is a band of a single color, interrupted by dark bands. The color seen is the color of the filter.

2. Describe what you saw when looking at the lamp through a double slit with no colored filters. Describe what you saw when looking at the lamp through a double slit covered with colored filters.

   With no filter, the pattern includes all the colors of the spectrum extending out from a central white area. With a filter, there is a band of a single color (the filter color), interrupted by dark bands.

3. Do your observations support the hypothesis that light possesses the properties of waves? Explain how the evidence you have uncovered supports your answer.

   They support the hypothesis since interference is a wave phenomenon.

4. How does the color of the filters affect your observations? Explain any variations observed.

   The spacing of the monochromatic bands varies with the color of the filter. The variations appear to be determined by the wavelength of light being transmitted.

CHAPTER
20 Critical Thinking

LIGHTNING

Using the *Reader's Guide to Periodical Literature* in your school library, find articles dealing with lightning. Read several of them to help you answer the following questions about lightning. List your reference at the end of each answer.

1. What are the chances of survival if you are struck by lightning?

Depending on the circumstances, the chances are two out of three for survival.

2. How does the number of deaths caused by lightning compare with the number of deaths due to other weather events such as tornadoes and hurricanes?

Lightning accounts for more deaths than the combined numbers for tornadoes and hurricanes.

3. What are some safety rules when dealing with lightning?

Never become a point of discharge. Avoid standing in an open space and avoid standing near tall objects.

4. How does a lightning rod protect a house?

A lightning rod provides a path for charges to flow directly to ground, without passing through the house. This protects the house from damage as a result of a lightning strike.

5. Identify each of the following types of lightning.
   a. forked lightning

   lightning from cloud to Earth or Earth to cloud

   b. sheet lightning

   lightning from cloud to cloud or cloud to upper atmosphere

   c. heat lightning

   lightning that is so far away that one does not hear the associated thunder

   d. bead or chain lightning

   forked lightning that is broken instead of a solid bright line

---

CHAPTER
21 Critical Thinking

A JARFUL OF CHANGE

Electric charges can be collected in a jar. The drawing shows a Leyden jar. It is made by covering the inner and outer surfaces of a glass jar with separate pieces of metal foil. A metal rod, with a metal knob at the end, protrudes through the stopper on top of the jar, and a metal chain connected to the rod touches the metal foil inside the jar. If a rubber rod is rubbed with fur and touched to the metal knob on the top of the Leyden jar, a negative charge is transferred to the inside of the jar. A positive charge develops on the outside of the jar.

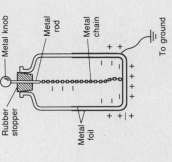

Metal knob
Metal rod
Metal chain
Rubber stopper
Metal foil
To ground

1. On the drawing provided, show the charge distribution on all metal parts of the Leyden jar.

2. Contrast the way a charge is given to the inside of the jar with the way a charge is given to the outside of the jar.

The inside of the jar is charged by conduction because the metal knob is touched by the charged rod. This charge spreads over the metal chain and foil because they are all in contact with each other. The outside of the jar is charged by induction, because it is not touched by a charged object. Instead, the negative charge inside the jar repels negative charges on the outside of the jar, inducing a positive charge.

3. Why must separate pieces of metal foil be used to cover the two surfaces of the jar?

If one continuous piece of metal foil were used, the negative charge given to the knob would spread over both surfaces of the jar. There would be no positive charge on the outer surface, so no potential difference would develop.

4. Why would the jar be unable to hold charges if there were no metal foil on the inside and outside of the jar?

The jar would be unable to hold a charge if there were no metal foil because glass is a poor conductor. Without the foil, a charge given to the metal knob would not flow throughout the jar.

5. What is the purpose of connecting the outside of the jar to the ground?

The outer surface of the jar is connected to the ground so that negative charges can flow away from the outer surface of the jar when they are repelled by the negative charges inside the jar.

6. Why would it be dangerous for you to touch the outside of the Leyden jar and the metal knob at the same time?

The human body is a conductor, and can become a pathway for electrons to flow to the ground. Touching a highly-charged Leyden jar could result in a dangerous discharge through the body.

7. Why are birds and squirrels able to sit on overhead electric wires without being electrocuted?

These animals are not in contact with the ground, so no discharge takes place when they touch the wires.

CHAPTER 22 Critical Thinking

FUTURE ENERGY USES

A highly industrialized society such as that of the United States requires tremendous amounts of energy to provide for the needs of its people. Most of the energy is made available from four sources: oil, coal, natural gas, and electricity. Moreover, the first two sources, oil and coal, are used to produce a large proportion of the electricity consumed in the United States.

Scientists, engineers, and conservationists have made many predictions concerning the future energy needs of the United States and how those energy needs might be satisfied. The table is an adaptation of one such projection. Increases in energy use are projected for the year 2010, taking into account various possible energy policies. "Other uses" include energy that is wasted. Examine the table and then answer the questions that follow.

Table 1

Energy conservation policy	Projected Energy Use				
	Buildings (%)	Industry (%)	Transport (%)	Other uses (%)	Increase from 1975 (%)
1. Make major lifestyle changes.	10.3	44.8	17.2	27.7	81.7
2. Make some lifestyle changes.	13.5	37.8	18.9	29.8	104.2
3. Slowly increase energy-producing efficiency.	13.8	35.1	21.3	29.8	132.4
4. Do not change present policies.	14.7	28.7	19.1	37.5	234.5

1. With regard to energy waste, what two policies produce the same result? What might explain this fact?

   policies 2 and 3; Efficiency would tend to reduce energy losses. Making "some lifestyle changes" would tend to increase energy conservation. Apparently, both of these policies would have approximately the same net effect on energy availability

2. What factor is projected to increase, regardless of the policy adopted? What reasons might you suggest for this?

   total energy demand; Total energy demand will increase as population increases and as a more affluent society demands more products. Increased construction of private homes, apartment buildings, and office buildings will increase the demand for energy in the buildings category.

3. Give your interpretation of "major lifestyle changes."

   Answers will vary, but will probably include dramatic reduction in the use of electrical appliances, such as dishwashers, television sets, air conditioners, and clothes dryers; reduction of the number of cars owned by a family, or the purchase of small fuel-efficient cars; reduction in travel for business and pleasure; increased use of mass transit.

CHAPTER 22 Critical Thinking

4. Give your interpretation of "some lifestyle changes."

   Answers will vary, but will probably include converting, where applicable, from electric home heating and cooking to natural gas or oil; moderate reduction in the use of electrical appliances such as electric clothes dryers, dishwashers, and television sets; lowering thermostat settings in homes and buildings during cold months and raising thermostat settings during hot months; car pooling.

5. A very large proportion of the energy produced today to meet the demands listed in the table come from the burning of fossil fuels. Choose one alternate source of energy from the following list and discuss the advantages and disadvantages of its use versus that of fossil fuels: geothermal energy, solar energy, nuclear energy, wind energy, tidal energy, hydroelectric energy.

   Although answers will vary, each should address at least the following criteria: availability at a particular locality; cost; and environmental effects, including effects on air, land, and water.

CHAPTER
23 : Critical Thinking

BREAKING A CIRCUIT

The circuit breaker illustrated and discussed in your text has a switch that includes a bimetallic strip. The circuit breaker shown here makes use of the magnetic field that is produced when a current flows through a wire. A coil of current-carrying wire that produces a magnetic field is called an electromagnet. In this circuit breaker, the electromagnet acts as a switch.

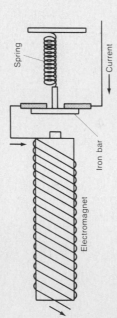

Spring

Electromagnet

Iron bar

→ Current

1. When current flows through the coil, the electromagnet exerts a force on the iron bar. The diagram shows another object that exerts a force on the iron bar. Identify that object.

   The spring exerts a force on the iron bar, holding it in place.

2. What happens to the amount of current in a circuit as more and more appliances are in use in that circuit?

   The amount of current increases.

3. As the current increases, the strength of the magnetic field increases, and the iron bar is pulled to the electromagnet. How does this action open the circuit?

   The iron bar is part of the circuit. When it is pulled out of position, the two elements that touched the bar are no longer connected, and the circuit is open.

4. The circuit breaker shown in your text does not make use of an electromagnet. What effect of electric current is the basis for the bimetallic-strip circuit breaker shown in the text?

   The circuit breaker shown in the text uses the heating effect of electric current.

5. In what way are the two types of circuit breakers similar?

   Both circuit breakers make use of effects that increase as the current increases. In the bimetallic-strip circuit breaker, the increase in current bends the strip, opening the circuit. In the electromagnet circuit breaker, the increase in magnetic force pulls the iron bar away from its contacts, opening the circuit.

CHAPTER
24 : Critical Thinking

THE DOORBELL

The diagram shows a doorbell that has an electromagnet as its main component.

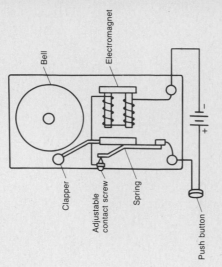

Bell

Electromagnet

Clapper

Adjustable contact screw

Spring

Push button

1. Starting from the positive terminal of the battery, name the components of the circuit through which the electric current will pass when the doorbell rings.

   battery, push button switch, spring, contact screw, electromagnet, battery

2. When the push button is used, a surge of current flows through the circuit. What effect does the electromagnet have on the spring and clapper assembly?

   The electromagnet will attract the spring and clapper, causing the clapper to move to the right and hit the bell.

3. When the clapper hits the bell, the spring will no longer be touching the contact screw. What effect will this have on the flow of current and the electromagnet?

   When the spring no longer touches the contact screw, the current stops flowing and the electromagnet stops attracting the spring and clapper.

4. Why does the clapper keep hitting the bell repeatedly as long as the button is pushed?

   When the spring touches the contact screw, the electromagnet pulls the clapper to the right to hit the bell. This breaks the circuit at the contact screw, turning off the electromagnet, and allows the spring to move the clapper to the left. This process repeats as long as current flows (when the button is pushed) and stops (when the circuit breaks at the contact screw).

5. Many doorbells have adjustable contact screws which can vary the distance between the spring and clapper assembly and the electromagnet. This permits the doorbell to function over a range of operating voltages. If a bell has been operating at 16 V and must now be used in a 12-V system, what changes would you make in the contact screw adjustment and explain why this is necessary?

   The contact screw must be adjusted to reduce the gap between the electromagnet and spring. Since the bell must operate on a lower voltage, the electromagnet will be weaker than before and may not be able to pull the spring and clapper to the right if they are too far away.

6. What other electrical devices use the doorbell's system to rapidly switch an electromagnet on and off?

   buzzers, ticker timers, automobile horns

CHAPTER
25 Critical Thinking

THE ELECTRIC GENERATOR

A generator contains an armature, which consists of a number of loops of wire wrapped around an iron core. The armature is spun in a magnetic field. In the diagram shown below, a single loop of wire represents a coil made up of many loops.

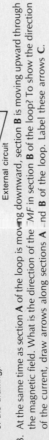

Direction of spin

1. What is the direction of the magnetic field? To represent this field, draw a single arrow, labeled **M**, on the diagram.

   The direction of the field is from right to left, or N-pole to S-pole.

2. Since the armature is spinning clockwise, the section of the loop labeled **A** is moving downward through the magnetic field. Using a right-hand rule, determine if the *EMF* is toward or away from you in this section of the wire.

   The *EMF* is away from you (toward the rear of the drawing).

3. At the same time as section **A** of the loop is moving downward, section **B** is moving upward through the magnetic field. What is the direction of the *EMF* in section **B** of the loop? To show the direction of the current, draw arrows along sections **A** and **B** of the loop. Label these arrows **C**.

   The *EMF* is toward you (toward the front of the diagram).

4. The loop is connected to the external circuit by a split-ring commutator, which is in contact with two brushes. Through which brush is current entering the external circuit?

   The current enters the external circuit through brush **X**.

5. After turning through one half of a rotation, section **A** of the loop will be moving upward and section **B** will be moving downward. What effect will this have on the direction of the current in the loop?

   The current in the loop reverses with each half rotation.

6. The one-half rotation puts loop section **A** in contact with brush **X**, and loop section **B** in contact with brush **Y**. What effect does this have on the direction of current in the external circuit?

   The current in the external circuit continues to move in the same direction.

7. A loop of current-carrying wire wrapped around an iron core forms an electromagnet. Use a right-hand rule to determine the N-pole and S-pole of the electromagnet formed by the spinning armature in the diagram. Label them **N** and **S**.

   The top end of the armature becomes the N-pole, and the bottom end becomes the S-pole.

CHAPTER
26 Critical Thinking

THE MICROWAVE OVEN

You have seen that a coil and a capacitor can be used to generate an oscillating field. However, there is a limit to the frequency of oscillation from such a unit. A device that produces a higher-frequency oscillation is the magnetron, which is the source of electromagnetic waves in a microwave oven. The magnetron consists of a central cathode surrounded by an anode block. The anode block contains a series of cavities, which function as resonating chambers. A strong magnet produces a magnetic field around the cathode and anode block. When electrons are emitted by the cathode, the magnetic field accelerates the electrons into a circular path. Electrons strike the openings to the cavities, and lose kinetic energy to the cavities, which oscillate. Meanwhile, the electrons return to the cathode. The frequency of the oscillation determines the frequency of the electromagnetic wave produced.

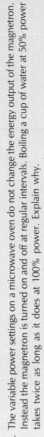

Cavity resonators

Anode block

Cathode

1. The walls of the resonating cavities develop a magnetic field, and the space between the walls develops an electric field. How is this similar to the coil-and-capacitor unit in an oscillator?

   In the coil-and-capacitor unit, the coil develops a magnetic field and the capacitor develops an electric field.

2. Why does the magnetron produce only one frequency of electromagnetic wave? How does this affect the amount of energy it can produce for heating food?

   The size of the resonating chamber determines the frequency of its oscillation, and the frequency of the electromagnetic wave produced. This means the microwave oven can only operate at full power.

3. The variable power settings on a microwave oven do not change the energy output of the magnetron. Instead the magnetron is turned on and off at regular intervals. Boiling a cup of water at 50% power takes twice as long as it does at 100% power. Explain why.

   At 50% power, the magnetron operates for approximately half the time.

4. If you have a microwave oven, you can determine the length of the on-and-off cycle that varies the power. Design a method to make this determination.

   Answers will vary. One method is described here. Place a microwave-safe measuring cup of water in the microwave, and heat it to boiling. Then observe the water as the microwave is set to various power levels. Notice how long the water is actively boiling versus how long it is still. While the magnetron is operating, thermal energy develops in the water, and the water boils. While the magnetron is not operating, no additional heat is being developed in the water, and so no boiling occurs.

   Students who have microwave ovens at home may wish to try this test. Remind them to use the microwave with caution and follow the manufacturer's instructions.

CHAPTER 27 Critical Thinking

STEP BY STEP

You know that electrons orbit the nucleus of an atom. When an electron absorbs energy, it moves to another energy level, which is farther from the nucleus. According to quantum theory, an electron cannot absorb just any amount of energy, or move into just any energy level. The electron makes a "quantum leap." It cannot move only part of the way.

A staircase can give you an idea of how energy is quantized. Imagine a staircase in which each step is 0.20 m higher than the preceding step. You have a 0.50-kg block, which you can place on any step. The potential energy of the block can be calculated using the equation $PE = mgh$. The potential energy at the floor level is 0 because h is equal to 0.

1. To what energy level in an atom does the floor at the base of the stairs correspond? Explain your answer.

   The floor corresponds to the ground state, because it is the lowest possible position, or energy level.

2. How much energy must you give the block to raise it from the floor to the first step?

   $PE = mgh$
   $= (0.50 \text{ kg})(9.8 \text{ m/s}^2)(0.20 \text{ m})$
   $= 0.98 \text{ J}$

3. How much energy must you give the block to raise it from the floor to the second step?

   $PE = mgh$
   $= (0.50 \text{ kg})(9.8 \text{ m/s}^2)(0.40 \text{ m})$
   $= 2.0 \text{ J}$

4. Suppose the block were on the floor and you increased its energy by 0.36 J. How high above the floor could you move the block?

   $h = \dfrac{PE}{mg}$

   $= \dfrac{0.36 \text{ J}}{(0.50 \text{ kg})(9.8 \text{ m/s}^2)}$

   $= 0.073 \text{ m}$

5. Would this amount of energy raise the block to the next step? Explain your answer.

   No, this amount would raise the block only about a third of the distance to the first step. There is no step at a height of 0.073 m, so the block would end up on the floor.

6. How is the staircase like the quantum model of the atom?

   Each step in a staircase is at a specific height, without a gradual change between steps, just as there are specific energy levels in the quantum model.

7. How is the staircase different from the quantum model of the atom?

   Each step in a staircase is equally far from the steps above and below it. Thus, all one-step changes have an equal energy value. In the quantum model, changes in energy are not the same between all levels. Also, the block that was lifted 0.73 m would fall back to the floor. In the quantum model of the atom, an electron that receives less than a quantum of energy does not move and fall back; it remains in place.

CHAPTER 28 Critical Thinking

STAR SPECTRA

Spectrographic analysis is used by astronomers to determine the composition of stars. The spectrum of a star depends on the star's temperature and composition. No two stars have exactly the same spectrum. The top two spectra shown are star spectra. The other spectra were produced by individual elements.

1. What kind of spectra are the star spectra shown?

   They are absorption spectra.

2. What kind of spectra are those shown for the elements?

   They are emission spectra.

3. Approximately what wavelengths are found on the hydrogen spectrum?

   4100 Å, 4350 Å, 4840 Å, 6550 Å

4. Does hydrogen occur in the atmosphere of star A? Of star B?

   Hydrogen occurs in the atmospheres of both stars.

5. What is the atmospheric composition of star A?

   The atmosphere of star A includes sodium, helium, and hydrogen.

6. What is the atmospheric composition of star B?

   The atmosphere of star B includes mercury, helium, and hydrogen.

7. Which elements do not occur in the atmosphere of either star?

   Strontium and calcium are not found in either atmospheres.

CHAPTER 30
Critical Thinking

DISTANCE AND RADIOACTIVITY

Table 1 shows the results of an experiment in which radiation was detected by a Geiger-Mueller counter placed at various distances from a radioactive source. Before the radioactive source was brought in, the background level of radiation was found to be 41 counts per minute. The readings shown in Table 1 include the background count, and must be corrected before the data can be graphed.

Table 1

Distance (cm)	Activity (counts/min)	Corrected activity (counts/min)	1/Distance^2
4	745	704	0.0625
6	311	270	0.0278
8	217	176	0.0156
10	151	110	0.0100
12	111	70	0.0069
14	91	50	0.0051
16	85	44	0.0039

1. Prepare a graph of the corrected activity versus distance. What does the shape of the graph tell you about the relationship between measured activity and distance from the source?

   The graph is a hyperbola, and indicates an inverse relationship.

2. If you wanted to produce a graph of a linear relationship, what variables would you compare?

   A linear relationship exists between the reciprocal of the square of the distance and the corrected activity.

3. Using the data provided, find the values you need to graph the relationship that will provide a straight-line graph. Add the new data to Table 1. Prepare your graph.

4. Use your second graph to predict the activity at a distance of 9 cm from the source. Is this the amount that would be detected by the Geiger-Mueller counter? Explain your answer.

   The activity would be 125 counts/min. This is the corrected value. The value recorded would also include background radiation and would be 166 counts/min.

CHAPTER 29
Critical Thinking

REMOTE CONTROL

A wireless remote-control unit for a television set or a video recorder consists of a transmitter unit and a receiver unit. Each unit contains a diode and a microchip, as well as a source of current. Suppose you want to turn on the television. When you push the button on the transmitter, current flows to the microchip, or encoder. Here a series of electrical pulses are produced and sent to the diode. The pulses are in binary code, the "language" of computers and all chip-operated devices. The diode in the transmitter unit is a light-emitting diode, which produces flashes of infrared light in binary code. In the receiver unit, the flashes of infrared light strike a light-sensitive diode, called a photodiode. The photodiode produces electrical pulses in binary code. The microchip in this circuit serves as a decoder. After the signal is decoded, the receiver unit causes the correct change to occur in the television set. In this example, the current is turned on.

1. Why must you point the transmitter unit directly at the receiver unit?

   Light travels in a straight line, and does not spread out much. If the transmitter is not aimed at the receiver, the light beam will miss its target.

2. Is the LED forward biased or reverse biased? Explain your answer.

   The LED is forward biased. There is so little resistance to the current that there is excess energy, released as light, when electrons combine with holes at the junction.

3. Why are the pulses of light produced by the transmitter in the same coded form as the electrical pulses produced by the encoder?

   Electrons flow and combine with holes only when "pushed" by the pulses of current. For each pulse, there is a flash of light. In between pulses, there are no flashes.

4. The transmitter unit uses a battery as a source of current. When the batteries begin to wear out, the potential difference they create gradually decreases. What happens to the signal as the batteries begin to wear out? Explain your answer.

   Although the batteries weaken gradually, the signal will not weaken gradually. The emission of a photon is a quantum effect. It has a threshold. Once the battery is unable to reach the threshold, there will be no photon released. Until that time, the release of photons will occur.

5. When light strikes the photodiode, electrons are removed from atoms. What is the name of this effect?

   This is the photoelectric effect.

6. The removal of electrons from atoms in the photodiode increases the flow of current in the diode. Is this diode forward biased or reverse biased? Explain your answer.

   This diode is reverse biased. Although it is connected to a source of current (if the television is plugged into the house current), little current flows through the diode. It takes extra energy, in the form of light pulses, to cause the flow of current.

CHAPTER
31 Critical Thinking

THE PENETRATING POWER OF RADIATION

Different types of radiation differ in their abilities to penetrate matter. Alpha particles are the most easily blocked. One sheet of cardboard can be enough to block alpha radiation. Beta particles are more penetrating. Gamma rays are the most penetrating form of radiation.

In this exercise, you will analyze the results of a test of the effect of the thickness of the shielding material on the penetrating power of beta radiation. A source of beta radiation was placed near a Geiger-Mueller tube, and the activity was measured. Then sheets of shielding materials were placed between the source and the Geiger-Mueller tube. The distance between the source and the tube was kept constant. The results are recorded in Table 1. These data have been corrected for background radiation. Study the data and answer the questions that follow.

Table 1

Number of sheets	0	1	2	4	6	8	10	12	14
				Activity Measured Through Shielding (counts/min)					
Cardboard	1000	756	633	444	311	217	152	106	75
Aluminum	1000	616	499	328	215	141	93	61	40
Lead	1000	518	355	110	45	10	1	—	—

1. What was the purpose of measuring the activity with no shielding material in place?

   This reading provided a reference reading so that a comparison could be made between the total amount of radiation being emitted and the amount penetrating the shield.

2. Why was it important to keep the distance between the source and the Geiger-Mueller tube constant?

   The measured activity decreases as the distance from the source increases. If the distance were not kept constant, there would be two variables involved—distance and shielding.

3. What happened to the activity readings as more sheets of shielding materials were placed between the source and the Geiger-Mueller tube? How would you explain these data?

   As the shielding was increased, the measured activity decreased. Beta particles were being absorbed by the shielding materials.

4. Which material was most effective in blocking radiation? What assumption must you make before using the data as a basis for your answer?

   Lead was the most effective shield. This comparison assumes that all the pieces of shielding material were the same thickness.

5. Prepare a graph of activity versus number of sheets of shielding material. What is the relationship between the thickness of the shielding material and the measured activity? Is the relationship linear?

   The thicker the shield, the less activity will be measured. The relationship is not linear.

6. If you wanted to know the shielding effect of two pieces of lead, but had only cardboard to use, how many pieces of cardboard would be needed?

   About five pieces of cardboard would be needed.

CHAPTER
30 Critical Thinking

Activity vs Distance

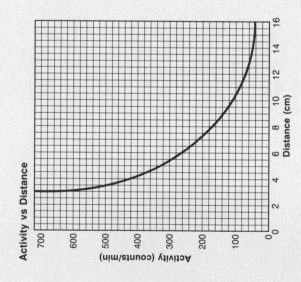

Activity vs $\dfrac{1}{\text{Distance}^2}$

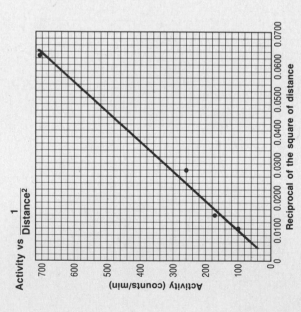

CHAPTER
31 Critical Thinking

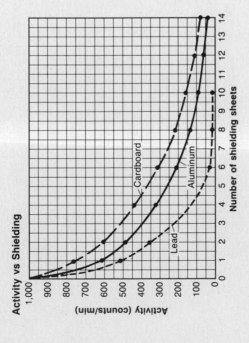

Activity vs Shielding

Cardboard

Aluminum

Lead

Activity (counts/min)

1,000
900
800
700
600
500
400
300
200
100
0

0 1 2 3 4 5 6 7 8 9 10 11 12 13 14

Number of shielding sheets

Notes